Practical Applications in
Appraisal Valuation Modeling

Appraisal Institute
Professionals Providing
Real Estate Solutions

Practical Applications in
Appraisal Valuation
Modeling

Statistical Methods for Real Estate Practitioners

by M. Steven Kane, Mark R. Linné, MAI, CRE, CAE, ASA, and Jeffrey A. Johnson, MAI

Appraisal Institute • 550 W. Van Buren •Suite 1000 • Chicago, IL 60607 • www.appraisalinstitute.org

Reviewers: Don M. Emerson, MAI, SRA
                 John A. Kilpatrick, PhD
                 Stephen A. Manning, MAI, SRA

Vice President, Educational Programs and Publications: Larisa Phillips
Director, Publications: Stephanie Shea-Joyce
Editor: Michael McKinley
Manager, Book Design/Production: Michael Landis
Production Specialist: Lynne Mattick-Payne
Senior Coordinator, Publications: Colette Nicolay

For Educational Purposes Only

The material presented in this text has been reviewed by members of the Appraisal Institute, but the opinions and procedures set forth by the author are not necessarily endorsed as the only methodology consistent with proper appraisal practice. While a great deal of care has been taken to provide accurate and current information, neither the Appraisal Institute nor its editors and staff assume responsibility for the accuracy of the data contained herein. Further, the general principles and conclusions presented in this text are subject to local, state, and federal laws and regulations, court cases, and any revisions of the same. This publication is sold for educational purposes with the understanding that the publisher is not engaged in rendering legal, accounting, or other professional service.

Nondiscrimination Policy

The Appraisal Institute advocates equal opportunity and nondiscrimination in the appraisal profession and conducts its activities in accordance with applicable federal, state, and local laws.

Printed in the United States of America

Library of Congress Cataloging-in-Publication Data
Kane, M. Steven.
      Practical applications in appraisal valuation modeling : by M. Steven Kane, Mark R. Linné, and Jeffrey A. Johnson.
         p. cm.
      Includes bibliographical references.
      ISBN 0-922154-79-1
      1. Real property–Valuation–Econometric models. 2. Valuation–Statistical methods. I. Linné, Mark R. II. Johnson, Jeffrey A. III. Title.

HD1387.K32 2003
333.33'2'015195–dc22

                                   2003070884

Table of Contents

About the Authors vi

Foreword vii

Acknowledgments viii

Preface ix

Chapter 1   The Whole Market 1

Chapter 2   Review of Statistical Analysis 13

Chapter 3   Data Exploration 25

Chapter 4   Describing Data 33

Chapter 5   Special Applications 55

Chapter 6   Market Trending Applications 79

Chapter 7   How to Mislead (i.e., Lie) With Statistics 99

Chapter 8   Modeling Applications 111

Chapter 9   Small Market Analysis 151

Chapter 10   Evaluating the Valuers 161

Chapter 11   Steps to Competence 173

Chapter 12   Resource Guide 179

Appendix 197

About the Authors

M. Steven Kane has previously worked as a statistical analyst in fields as widely varying as criminal justice, economics, and biometrics. For the past 10 years, he has applied his statistical training and experience to real estate appraisal, working as a consultant and fee appraiser concentrating on commercial property valuation of all types. He was the chief valuation architect for the first residential AVM product developed in Colorado. Mr. Kane is presently director of strategic development for RMVS/ValX. Mr. Kane has published numerous articles on the need for whole market valuation of real estate and the application of mass appraisal techniques in the appraisal profession as well as serving as co-author of the Appraisal Institute text *A Guide to Appraisal Valuation Modeling*. Mr. Kane was the developer of the Appraisal Institute's seminar on appraisal valuation modeling, which he has taught across the country. Mr. Kane is currently finishing his master's degree in real estate appraising from the University of St. Thomas.

Mark R. Linné, MAI, CRE, CAE, ASA, Managing Director of RMVS/ValX, has a varied background in appraisal. He has been active in the development of adaptive valuation technologies including automated valuation models (AVMs) and was a member of the development team responsible for the creation of one of the first AVMs, capable of valuing over 750,000 residential properties along the Colorado Front Range. He has served as vice chair of *The Appraisal Journal* Review Board and on several Appraisal Institute national committees. Mr. Linné was one of the original members of the Ad-Hoc Committee on Computer-Assisted Appraisal for the International Association of Assessing Officers (IAAO), and he has served two terms on the Colorado State Board of Assessment Appeals. In addition to co-authoring *A Guide to Appraisal Valuation Modeling*, Mr. Linné has written numerous articles on statistical analysis and the future of appraising for *Valuation Insights & Perspectives, Assessment Digest,* and the *Colorado Real Estate Journal,* and he was the recipient of the Donohoo Award for the best article on assessment.

Jeffrey A. Johnson, MAI, is an appraiser and principal with Integra Realty Resources in Minneapolis, Minnesota. He has a master of science degree in mathematics. He is co-instructor of the Statistical Analysis for Real Estate Appraisal course in the master's degree program at the University of St. Thomas. He developed the Appraisal Practices for Litigation seminar for the Appraisal Institute in 1993 and was a corecipient of the 2001 George L. Schmutz Memorial Award in recognition of his work on the development of the 12th edition of *The Appraisal of Real Estate.* He serves as chair of the Educational Publications Committee of the Appraisal Institute. Mr. Johnson focuses his appraisal practice on litigation matters.

Foreword

The modern real estate appraiser is drowning in a sea of data. The challenge today is managing and analyzing the torrent of data, whereas the process of gathering data once dominated an appraiser's workday. Technological tools and sophisticated analytical techniques have emerged to help appraisers keep their heads above water, but many traditionalists are suspicious—or even hostile—to those innovations in appraisal methodology. *Practical Applications in Appraisal Valuation Modeling: Statistical Methods for Real Estate Practitioners* charts new territory and illustrates how the statistical analysis once used only in mass appraisal and in the classroom has real-world applications—and how it may become an essential component of every appraisal in the future.

A resource for skeptical valuation veterans and curious newcomers alike, the Appraisal Institute's latest text on statistics builds on the base of *A Guide to Appraisal Valuation Modeling*, a guidebook by the same authors that introduced the subject to readers. The new book delves deeper into the statistician's bag of tricks and takes the reader through the analytical process step by step, from the initial exploratory data analysis through linear regression modeling, using the types of real estate situations and data appraisers commonly encounter. The benefits and pitfalls of the use of statistical modeling are examined, so that appraisers will be able to express their value opinions more clearly and persuasively and also judge when someone is manipulating the statistics—for example, when an automated statistical package is providing misleading information.

The authors see the perceived "threat" of automated valuation models (AVMs) taking business away from established valuation professionals as an opportunity for the appraisal community to diversify its activities and move into the twenty-first century. To meet the challenges of the evolving business environment, appraisers will need to leverage the enabling technology of appraisal valuation models to improve their operational efficiency and analytical sophistication. A process of self-education using *Practical Applications in Appraisal Valuation Modeling* (with additional resources for further study prominently featured in the book) serves as the first step on the road to competency with the expanded appraisal tool kit.

Gary P. Taylor, MAI, SRA
2004 President
Appraisal Institute

Acknowledgments

This book has been a collaborative process in the truest sense of the word. The authors were assisted by the editorial and technical staff of the Appraisal Institute and others in the appraisal profession to define important concepts and develop the methodologies presented on the following pages. Many of these concepts may seem new at first glance, but in reality we are simply applying a different type of brushstroke to the appraisal canvas.

We would like to extend our thanks for the efforts of the Appraisal Institute's Publications staff. Stephanie Shea-Joyce, Michael McKinley, Michael Landis, and Colette Nicolay were all instrumental. Each provided specific inputs to the book you now hold. We would also like to give special thanks to John Schwartz, the 2003 Chair of the Educational Publications Committee, as well as the reviewers of this text. All were supportive and crucial contributors.

We need to also acknowledge the roles of those who inspired us along the way. This includes Robert Gloudemans (the master of it all), Garth Thimgan (who knows how to do it from the assessment side), John Ross (who simply knows everything), Alan Hummel (who defines what leadership needs to be), and John Cirincione (who knows how to get it done from the private-sector side). They represent the future and the course that needs to be followed. Listen well.

Most critically, we recognize the patience and support of our families. Authoring a book requires a remarkable amount of time spent away from those who matter most.

Finally, we would like to thank Nikell Brinkmann for "the quote."

To those who read this book with the goal of understanding, welcome aboard. To those who read it with a critical eye and find a better way, bravo. To those who think that things will stay the same in our profession, watch out.

There's change in the air. . .

Preface

"A professional always specializes."

– Richard Farnsworth, as a former stagecoach
robber turned train robber, *The Grey Fox* (1982)

There has long existed a dichotomy within the appraisal profession: essentially the partitioning of the appraisal worldview between mass appraisal and single-property appraisal. Both disciplines, to some extent, have been myopic with respect to the techniques and perspectives of the other. In many ways, this partitioning inhibits the transference of knowledge between the two. Assessment practitioners, charged with the simultaneous valuation of thousands of commercial and residential properties, have had to develop perspectives and techniques that enable them to process myriad data points into a reasonable and defensible framework. Conversely, fee appraisers have traditionally focused on fewer data points to develop their estimates of value. There is clear evidence that the roles of the two disciplines are rapidly converging with the integration of statistical techniques and data availability.

–A Guide to Appraisal Valuation Modeling (2000)

In the three years since the publication of *A Guide to Appraisal Valuation Modeling*, authors M. Steven Kane and Mark R. Linné have seen the techniques of mass appraisal and single-property appraisal continue to converge. Notable examples include the grafting of a private sector AVM module to a computer-assisted mass appraisal (CAMA) assessment system and the extension of public sector development standards to the private sector. Further proof of this convergence can be seen in the standardization of experience and techniques and the integration of valuation processes and ideas among a multitude of appraisal organizations.

The first AVM guide introduced readers to the concepts of valuation modeling for the appraisal of real property, reacquainting them with basic statistical techniques and methodology. This new book, which has an additional author, Jeffrey A. Johnson, will help appraisers incorporate statistical analyses into their everyday practice. It poses valuation problems, suggests appropriate analyses, and offers practical solutions.

The fee appraisal and assessment communities are currently testing many different techniques that have evolved from mass appraisal analysis. This book synthesizes the current applications, focusing less on theory and more on practical techniques that appraisers can employ immediately to solve valuation problems ranging from discerning market trends to determining adjustments for physical property attributes. Integrating a structured statistical analysis format into the valuation process transforms large data sets into valuable information.

There is strong demand for competency in statistical analyses for valuation purposes. To acquire such competence, appraisers must gain confidence in their ability to manipulate large data sets. Hands-on training with the statistical functions of programs such as Microsoft Excel and statistical software such as SPSS and Minitab is crucial for that purpose. This book promotes interactive education and illustrates the complex analyses that would be impossible using a handheld calculator.

This book, like *A Guide to Appraisal Valuation Modeling* and the existing Appraisal Institute AVM seminar, integrates real-world appraisal experience and statistical analysis, providing the best exposure to the subject for fee appraisers and others interested in single-property valuation. A later chapter will examine the basic competence level required of appraisers using appraisal valuation modeling applications. The current competency requirements set forth in USPAP and in professional licensing and certification curricula have not been developed fully enough to provide specific guidance, and, given the growing, pervasive use of AVM products in the marketplace, competency needs to be more formally addressed than it is today.

Appraisers today may be asked to use software that purports to calculate property values from vendor-supplied AVMs. Clients with access to such products may need appraisers to explain, augment, or review the output. An appraiser must understand the basics of these valuation products to use them effectively and confidently. There are ways to integrate these fixed or adjustable models into more accurate, more reliable value conclusions.

In the future, we believe the statistical analyses illustrated in *Practical Applications in Appraisal Valuation Modeling* will augment one of the three traditional approaches to value and may even become an integrated approach to value of its own. Appraisers, investors, underwriters, and litigators must become proficient in statistical analysis and extend their mathematical competence if they want to enhance their skills as appraisers, analysts, and users of these services. Their future success will depend on it.

How to Use This Book

The application chapters in this book move toward regression-based valuation modeling as a goal. Along the way readers will learn how to describe collections of data (i.e., size, ranges, patterns, averages) and specific ways to measure differences between data (e.g., measuring external effects on one neighborhood by comparing it to a similar neighborhood).

The case studies and examples presented throughout the book consider both residential and commercial situations. Markets for special-use properties, mixed-use properties, and properties with detrimental conditions or one-of-a-kind features can be modeled with these techniques as well. Statistical analysis can be used in product marketing and to determine consumer spending patterns as well as in areas where human behavior can be measured quantitatively (or described qualitatively) with defined outcomes. Such analyses can be descriptive, inferential, or both; the differences between these two types of analyses will be explained in more detail later. Descriptive data techniques, measures, and statistical tests can apply to both income-motivated and amenity-motivated property.

To provide a guide through the modeling process, the navigation chart illustrated on the following page will be referenced throughout the book. This text stops at regression modeling. Advanced applications include non-linear modeling, GIS applications, feedback systems, and unified valuation modeling. Some of these are under development, some have been in use for years, and all warrant more sophisticated discussion than the space here allows. They will be left for future appraisers and analysts to investigate.

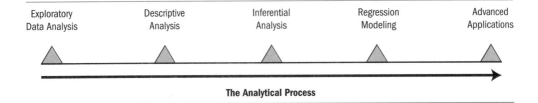

| Exploratory Data Analysis | Descriptive Analysis | Inferential Analysis | Regression Modeling | Advanced Applications |

The Analytical Process

A solid understanding of the linear regression process provides a foundation for further investigation into more complex–and more reliable–procedures. Note that most real-world market phenomena observed at a point in time can best be explained as a matrix of linear relationships. The process of purchasing a home is often modeled mathematically as a linear event in which potential buyers add positive and negative factors for each buying option. Factors such as location, physical characteristics, and externalities influence individual buyers, who in turn shape the market by their actions. Statistical analysis recognizes the probabilistic nature of such market factors and can help relate them to value.

One final note: many fee appraisers already use statistical techniques, particularly descriptive tools, in their analyses. They have demonstrated that these methods are appropriate and practical for the appraisal profession. To many such professionals, the procedures described in this book will seem familiar, although the array of possible applications may come as a surprise. What goes on inside the head of an appraiser is quite akin to statistical modeling. For lack of a more scientific name, it has been called the art of appraisal.

CHAPTER 1

The Whole Market

"Beware of what you wish for because you might get it."
– author unknown

Since the first days of the real estate valuation profession, it seems that fee appraisers have had to scrounge for data. Now that they finally have what they wished for, they face a brand-new problem–how to manage the overabundance of data and extract meaningful, accurate information from the data without drowning in it.

Historically, many appraisers were content to value residential and commercial properties alike using the three to five most comparable sales they could find. Rental data was limited, and market cost data was often simply unavailable. Yet despite the dearth of data, valuation theory and methodology still progressed, and sophisticated applications were developed by the giants of the profession based on analysis of real-world market behavior. Armed with the latest techniques, the current generation of appraisers tackle intricate and challenging valuation problems that concern economic, locational, physical, and even temporal attributes of the subject property. But mechanical veracity matters little if appraisers continue to use small portions of the entire range of data available from the *whole market*–i.e., the complete, unabridged data set.

Today appraisers have access to a much greater amount of market data than in the past. This does not just apply to comparable sales data. Rental data, cost data, and market trend and economic supply and demand data are now typically available in amounts that can literally overwhelm manual adjustment techniques, even though those techniques are fundamentally sound. Some industry experts have demonstrated that the human mind cannot process more than a few data points consistently and comprehensively. When adjustments to those data points add a new dimension to the analysis, it becomes impossible to effectively

Drowning in Data

Average Depth 6 Inches

whole market analysis
Appraisal analysis using all relevant market data based on appraisal valuation principles. The scope can range from a few sales to many sales; the determination is based on valuation relevance, not the physical limitations of the valuation methods used (i.e., manual analysis versus statistical analysis).

balance and consider all of the iterative steps to derive a rational and defensible valuation conclusion.

A growing body of new appraisal theory and valuation methodology addresses the "whole market" issue. Much of this progressive thought, as discussed in *A Guide to Appraisal Valuation Modeling* and in other works, is based on statistical methods, the branch of mathematics that analyzes trends and relationships between variables. As with most new methods, there has been a backlash to this trend. Some appraisers interpret the infiltration of statistics and modeling as simply attempts to add an additional layer to a process and a profession already overwhelmed by analytical methods, producing so-called "analysis paralysis." This subset of traditionalist appraisers demands that proponents of new techniques not only demonstrate the applicability of these new methods (the "how to") but also explain why they are necessary in the first place.

These demands are completely reasonable. It makes no sense for appraisers to use a new technique for the sake of the technique itself. An even more pertinent question is why should appraisers use these new techniques when their clients, even the more sophisticated ones, are content with traditional appraisals using three to five sales, four rent comparables, and no market cost data? In other words, why bother if there is no perceived need?

This book addresses these very questions. The simple answer is that appraisers must consider all appropriate data available from the market. Picking the four or five sales an appraiser thinks are the most comparable out of a data set like the one shown in Table 1.1 will not do. Professional standards dictate that all pertinent evidence must be presented and reasoned analysis must be included in appraisals. The "trust me" approach no longer suffices.

Current Appraisal Practice and AVM Development

Real estate appraisal practice has undergone significant changes since the inception of the Uniform Standards of Professional Appraisal Practice (USPAP). This body of standards was implemented in 1989 after appraisal abuses contributed in part to the real estate downturn of the 1980s. Up to that point, appraisal licensing requirements were virtually nonexistent and standards of practice varied widely from state to state. USPAP was a product of the Financial Institutions Reform, Recovery, and Enforcement Act

Table 1.1   An Overabundance of Market Data

Address	Sale Price	Sale Date	Improved Area	Lot Size	Days on Market
7600 S Vaughn Ct	$1,622,000	5/29/1998	25,921	1.98	10
2130–2140 S Lipan St	485,000	10/8/1999	12,441	0.43	39
9885 Brighton Rd	41,500	9/27/1999	7,773	3.2295	16
2 Lipan St	265,000	1/13/1999	6,700	0.1745	31
12225 E 39th Ave	3,650,000	10/1/2001	130,057	10.563	31
4701 National Western Dr	540,000	6/18/2001	18,540	0.621	83
1397 W Cedar Ave	300,000	10/9/2001	4,430	0.301	22
7074 S Revere Pkwy	22,631,000	7/21/2000	18,550	1.203	0
3354 Larimer St	310,000	12/26/2001	2,500	0.2847	29
7076 S Alton Way #H	6	1999	7,892		20
7006-E S Alton Way #E			7,880	0.1837	19
10302 S Progress Way			8,512	1	13
38 E 5th Ave		01	40,518	0.861	65
9844 W Titan Park Cir	1,685,000	5/ /2000		0.72	15
7076 S Alton Way Bldg G	875,000	10/23/2000			21
1385-1395 S Inca St	750,000			0.637	40
2635 Walnut St	710,00			0.2873	47
13301 W 43rd Dr	425,1				1
3801 E 56th Ave	395,			0.92	3
480 Yuma St	285			0.2018	14
3835 E 48th Ave	41			2.2507	48
3601 S Natches Ct	250			1.935	96
5505 Central Ave	1,850,0			0.3926	24
7399 S Tucson Way	7,440,			10	8
15350, 15353, 15357 E Hinsdale	2,190,000			3	
5155 E 46th Ave	1,900,000	12/		3.8196	25
200 E 64th Ave	900,000	5/1/1998	12	2.5568	26
2075 S Valentia St	760,000	12/11/1998	,84	1.2081	
7551 & 7561 S Grant St	565,000	5/20/1999	0,0	2.175	15
99 E 68th Ave	350,000	3/15/1999	4,6	0.992	39
3898 Morrison Rd	315,000	12/4/1998	8,01	0.2631	
5775 Flatiron Pkwy	13,050,000	7/5/2000	95,74	5.246	13
14 Inverness Dr E	11,708,000	11/28/2001	15,2	14.023	27
9950 E Easter Ave	6,080,000	6/22/20	73,4	4.805	1
6837 Winchester Cir	6,000,000	1/1	74	7.1749	7
12154 N Dumont Way	2,500,000	1/2/2002		6.48	15
2525 W Evans Ave	1,850,000	1/18/2000	32,718	1.207	20
4730 Independence St	1,053,100	12/14/2000	14,288	4.022	30
2724 Walnut St	955,000	1/2/2002	15,723	0.4304	41
6035 E 38th Ave	772,540	10/10/2001	20,330	1.0638	21
820-826 Lincoln St	682,150	6/13/2001	19,800	0.643	18

Here is the data you requested.

(FIRREA) of 1989, which required states to certify and license appraisers for various types of appraisal assignments. Furthermore, the implementation of USPAP formalized appraisal practice. Specific valuation issues were addressed and methodologies were refined as a result. Today, the appraiser is armed with a strong body of theoretical knowledge to apply to valuation problems.

Yet even appraisers armed with current valuation methodologies face one of the most significant challenges in the profession today–the loss of market share caused by automated valuation model (AVM) systems. These systems use statistical models to derive real estate value, replacing flesh-and-blood appraisers. They also use all available market data, most often in the form of a database of comparable sales.

Evidence of the erosion of market share is clear. Since 1996 over 70% of the residential appraisal market in California has been "lost" to AVM systems. Banks in that state now use these products in place of residential appraisers in many instances. In 1998 the Federal Home Loan and Mortgage Corporation (Freddie Mac) implemented a desktop AVM system to determine the value of homes. This action reduced the demand for residential drive-by appraisals on a national scale. AVM systems once implemented for secondary residential financing have crept into the primary mortgage market as well. Even commercial appraisal demand is threatened by the advent of AVM technology, with several large national real estate firms now developing commercial AVM systems.

Automated Valuation Models Versus Appraisal Valuation Modeling

The distinction between *automated valuation models* and *appraisal valuation modeling* goes beyond mere words. Historically, AVM systems evolved from assessment valuation models, which value a large number of residential properties using statistical algorithms and mass appraisal theory.

Early AVM systems were tested during the late 1980s and early 1990s, but it was only when personal computing became powerful enough in the mid-1990s that widespread AVM development could be implemented by private firms. At that point in personal computer evolution, data processing speed and accuracy allowed desktop computers to handle property files with thousands of records. Standard, off-the-shelf statistical software, such as SPSS and Minitab, also became more powerful during this

> Appraisers *must* supplement their skill set with valuation methods that can systematically analyze larger data sets with output that is readily applicable to single-property appraisal. The importance of this cannot be overstated: AVM technology will replace most appraisers in the near future if appraisers do not adapt to the market.

period, allowing for the efficient manipulation of data. Problems with data transfer between assessment property records stored on mainframe computers and the desktop computers of AVM developers lingered, but these were eventually overcome.

When larger companies such as HNC entered the market in 1997, smaller firms saw their chances at large-scale success evaporate. Large corporations were able to invest significant sums of capital and hire analysts from both the assessment field and academia. The stage was set for full-scale development of AVM systems. All that was needed was a wide area network to relay results to clients nationally; this was hastened by the widespread use and acceptance of the Internet, completing the circle. By the end of the decade, AVM systems had evolved from small market "garage front" operations to true nationwide vendor systems.

Of course, not every market or every lender has embraced this new valuation technology. AVM systems have worked best in newer urban markets, such as California and Arizona. In regions where homes are older and less homogenous, such as the northeastern United States, these products have met with only limited success. This regionalism, however, is fading rapidly as newer modeling techniques are implemented and lenders invest additional millions of dollars into their systems.

Appraisal valuation modeling represents another evolutionary step in valuation technology and is significantly different than vendor-supplied AVM systems. First, it was developed to enhance, rather than replace, traditional appraisal methods. Second, this system is built on appraisal theory, using statistical methods as secondary tools. Finally, AVM methods integrate completely with current appraisal methods and conform to USPAP requirements concerning disclosure and demonstrable market veracity.

Developed by appraisers with both fee appraisal and assessment backgrounds, AVM methods use the strength found in mass appraisal modeling and combines it with the single-property techniques used in fee appraisal. For example, the valuation of single-family homes by mass appraisal typically involves many sales (50-500) and many variables (20-30), which are used together to value a whole range of properties in a predefined market area. This market area is often referred to as a *neighborhood*. Typical fee simple property appraisal, on the other hand, values one subject property using from three to six sales and from five to 10 variables. These variables and

Appraisal valuation modeling techniques augment traditional appraisal practice, which differentiates them from automated valuation model systems that literally replace the appraiser. The appraiser, therefore, is maintained as the valuation expert. A new term, *appraisal-centric valuation modeling*, is perhaps the most descriptive and accurate explanation for the AVM initials used by practitioners.

sales are manipulated in a grid, where appraisers manually adjust differences between comparable properties and the subject.

In appraisal valuation modeling, many sales are used, as with mass appraisal, but fewer variables are applied in the ensuing AVM models. The technique resembles the analytical process in fee appraisal. The statistical tests and modeling also resemble mass appraisal models, but the market modeling approach follows fee appraisal guidelines. The result is a true hybrid approach, using many sales to value a single property within market-based parameters. This methodology can be applied to income and cost data as well. All applications use the entirety of available, appropriate market data (i.e., the whole market) to derive value conclusions. This greater dynamism can impact both residential and commercial appraisals.

Residential Appraisal Applications

Residential appraisal today is primarily a volume-driven business. Given the smaller fees, which typically range between $75 and $350 per assignment, residential appraisers must turn out appraisal reports at the rate of one to two per day. In addition, the demands of the real estate market are such that clients often need residential appraisals within a matter of days.

Despite the challenges, most residential appraisers "get it right" in terms of valuation issues. Residential properties, for the most part, are simply more straightforward to value than other types of real estate. Sales data is plentiful–perhaps too plentiful–and electronic forms on personal computers make the production of reports fast and easy.

Economies of scale do help make residential fee appraisers more productive, but they also may make competing AVM systems even more of a threat. Since residential appraisal is so straightforward in its methodology, computer technology can create statistical models that replicate the appraisal process accurately. Often, these vendor AVM systems can value homes and condominiums in seconds, as opposed to hours or days. Even the most efficient fee appraiser cannot compete directly with AVM systems in terms of speed. Even worse, cost can be as low as $10 per AVM valuation in some markets.

The use of AVM systems does not come without potential risks, however. Canned AVM systems are notorious for their lack of appraisal output. Often the valuation of a property is presented with output statistics limited only to those "proving" the overall statistical fit of the model. The actual variables used to value the property may not be presented. A listing of comparable sales is also left out of most AVM output. The client is presented with an unverified value conclusion, which lacks much of the supporting information they have come to expect in a residential appraisal report.

To improve personal productivity, many residential appraisers currently rely on a disjointed collection of multiple automated systems that often cannot communicate with one another. This can create as many problems as it solves. Sales data from automated sources are literally entered by hand into electronic appraisal forms. Cost data is handled in the same manner. Appraisers have to manually sort data and determine which sales are "most comparable" to the subject property. No statistical or weighting schemes are employed to measure why, for example, Sales A, B, and C are more comparable to the subject than Sales D, E, and F. Often lender clients or homeowners question these comparable sale selections, and the appraisers have to answer questions instead of turning their attention to new assignments.

In contrast, appraisal valuation modeling methods include the application of standardized data files using all comparable sales, with predetermined valuation models and output. These models, of course, can be adjusted by the appraiser for the particular attributes of the subject property, but this process is standardized and replicable, using statistical weighting and reduction methods. All of this is controlled by an appraiser, who is guided by appraisal judgment. With such an integrated system, the output of appraisers can increase significantly. This in turn allows the appraiser to minimize (though not eliminate entirely) the relative advantage that competing AVM systems have in turnaround time.

In terms of appraisal quality, the same integration of data processing and valuation methodology provides more than a level playing field for residential appraisers facing vendor-based AVM competition. The primary difference is the appraiser's role. In vendor-supplied AVM systems, the statistical model drives the valuation process. With the appraisal valuation modeling approach advocated in this book, the appraiser drives the system, using statistical modeling guided by appraisal theory. In addition, the appraiser is given the opportunity to constantly review and verify the valuation process, which is not possible with vendor products. More importantly, in

There has been concern that many property valuations supplied by automated valuation models are inflated and not indicative of current market trends. This is because the output of an AVM is usually based on *historic* trends. This violates USPAP Standards Rule 1-4, which requires appraisers to use *all* available market data in their valuation analyses. Since tax assessment appraisers, under USPAP's Jurisdictional Exception Rule, often develop their CAMA models using historical sales data, they are not under the same USPAP requirements. Many private sector AVMs are based on similar modeling parameters, but the Jurisdictional Exception Rule does not apply.

cases where automated modeling does not work, the appraiser can still employ the current manual approach to render a defensible valuation.

The third and final way in which appraisal valuation modeling technology enhances residential appraisal concerns product scope. Vendor AVM systems, by their very nature, are capable of only a limited range of standard output. Most of the time, a single valuation method is employed to value one or more properties with a given set of data. The appraiser, on the other hand, can adapt to the market and offer a wider range of valuation services. Appraisers proficient in AVM methods can offer specialized valuation assignments such as consulting assignments involving mass appraisal thanks to their additional capabilities.

A variety of appraisal consulting services are made possible by appraisal valuation modeling techniques:

- Valuation problems concerning classes of properties or large area issues, such as the proximity of a potential detrimental condition, can be analyzed with greater sophistication than previously possible. For example, in the past the impact on property values of proximity to an EPA Superfund site could only be determined using paired sales analysis, a manual adjustment process in which the sale of a property close to the site would be compared to another sale of a similar property farther away. This method assumes that there are no significant differences among the other attributes of the two properties and that the result can be generalized to all properties in the market area. These assumptions are often unsubstantiated. Using this same example, an appraiser applying appraisal valuation modeling would select multiple homes, some with exposure to the location attribute and some away from the attribute. Statistical testing would allow for the quantification of any differential based on location proximity.
- Appraisers can verify the results of vendor AVM systems used by clients.
- Appraisers can derive market factors such as sales or housing price trends for clients. These can even be reported to local market media, thus creating exposure for appraisers as local real estate market experts.

All of these new products diversify the practices of residential appraisers and make them less sensitive to market fluctuations from business cycles and also less sensitive to market erosion by automated valuation modeling. The competitive advantage residential appraisers can gain depends on their ability to use all of the available market data.

Commercial Appraisal Applications

Ironically, the branch of appraisal least affected so far by the encroachment of private sector AVMs stands to gain the most from the use of appraisal valuation modeling techniques. The appraisal of commercial properties by its very nature is more complex and time-consuming than residential appraisal. Commercial assignments typically take weeks to complete, as opposed to days for residential work. Fees are also much greater. But where much is given, much more is expected.

Commercial appraisers often use all three approaches to value, whereas residential appraisers typically use only the cost and sales comparison approaches to value residential properties. The income capitalization approach, which is not used in residential appraisal, is the most complex and dynamic approach to value, and it involves many market inputs and adjustments. Also, market analysis is typically much more complex in commercial assignments.

Like the analysis that goes into the appraisal of commercial properties and real estate markets, commercial appraisal reports are much more complex. Residential reports are generally produced on forms that range from four to 10 pages, but narrative commercial reports can be well over 100 pages long. The data presented in commercial reports is complex and includes not only explicit data on the subject but also data on comparable sale properties and market area attributes.

The complexity that has insulated commercial appraisal from AVM encroachment so far is slowly being stripped away by mass appraisal practitioners. Market area data and comparable property data—for both sale and rental properties—have great modeling potential. In fact, large-scale econometric models have been developed in academia and in assessment circles for this purpose. The assessment world has also cracked the code in terms of commercial mass appraisal.

The major advantages of appraisal valuation modeling methods for residential appraisal also

Appraisal valuation modeling techniques can result in more unified processing of appraisal data. In addition, these methods provide easier and quicker access to Internet sources that provide both market and real estate economic data. They also allow for a whole market approach to real estate market and property analysis.

Faced with 30 or more sales, an appraiser cannot properly apply traditional approaches to select the five best sales or rental comparables from the market. A systematic evaluation of all sales and rents in a given market must be employed. More importantly, the appraiser must explain the rejection of any sales *not* used in the valuation analysis.

apply to commercial appraisal, perhaps even more so. Despite the much slower pace of workflow, commercial appraisal can benefit significantly from the use of these techniques today and protect against AVM's market assault tomorrow. Make no mistake about future private sector AVM advances in commercial appraisal markets: the question is not "if" but "when" they appear.

In a commercial appraisal shop using these new methods, the systematic development of comparable sale and lease data from previous appraisals can save appraisers hours of work time spent searching vendor databases and private appraisal files. In addition, the development time for narrative reports can be shortened using descriptive statistical tables and graphs. These can be generated using off-the-shelf software such as Excel and Lotus. More ambitious appraisers can invest modest amounts of additional time and money and use PC-based statistical software such as SPSS or MiniTab. Time spent developing complex adjustment grids by hand can be easily saved with valuation models that can handle a greater number of comparable sales and adjustment factors. New techniques save time and increase accuracy, eliminating errors based on manual adjustments.

Given the USPAP requirements that appraisers use all data "as are available" in the development of the three approaches to value, appraisers are often faced with too much data. In the manual adjustment process, adjustment factors quickly run up against their numeric limits. Current methodologies based on manual techniques are simply inadequate for dealing with large data sets. Even if a case can be made that the most appropriate comparable sales are within a certain range–say, eight to 10 comparable sales or rental comparables–appraisers still must be able to demonstrate that the reduction of the data pool to that level is sound and unbiased.

Another qualitative advantage of appraisal valuation modeling concerns how market data relates to the subject property. Commercial properties often present complex highest and best use problems. Under USPAP appraisers are typically required to demonstrate a single maximally productive use for the subject property, often from a wide range of development options. The linkage between pertinent market data and the highest and best use conclusions must also be demonstrable. AVM techniques can develop rational decision paths that are easily pre-

In addition to improvements in product efficiency and quality, the use of AVM techniques can expand the scope of work opportunities for appraisers. Ironically, some of these new services could involve the verification of automated valuation system output.

sented in a narrative report. They can also provide the client with strong econometric evidence of the feasibility or infeasibility of a particular land use.

Finally, like residential appraisers, commercial appraisers can leverage AVM techniques to

expand the scope of work they do. Commercial appraisers are already asked to perform consulting assignments related to market value appraisal, such as feasibility analyses and market studies. Other new opportunities include mass appraisal projects, such as urban redevelopment proposals and environmental reclamation. For example, one Atlanta-based appraisal firm conducted an analysis to develop market adjustment factors for vacant land adjacent to the Florida Everglades. These factors were then used to guide other appraisers who were assigned to value these vacant parcels. The data set for this study included more than 350 sales and 180 potential adjustment factors, numbers that would have crippled an appraiser applying manual adjustment techniques.

CHAPTER 2

Review of Statistical Analysis

"Those who do not remember the past are doomed to repeat it."

—George Santayana

Before charting the new territory of appraisal valuation modeling, a quick review of the basics of statistical analysis would be helpful. To aid in understanding and to allay any fears of the subject matter, the discussion of statistical theory in this chapter is framed in the context of real estate appraisal.

Statistical analysis is used to identify, measure, and interpret events in nature. These events, or *phenomena*, can be thought of as any measurable activity; in the case of real estate valuation, this activity involves human action, such as buying, selling, renting, or developing real property. Such phenomena are measured by monetary transactions or other quantitative indices, allowing the appraiser to categorize, gauge, and compare activities.

Components of Statistical Analysis

The following sections will examine the three components of statistical analysis from an appraisal perspective:

1. Identification
2. Quantification
3. Interpretation

For example, when an appraiser performs a typical sales comparison analysis, the market-relevant variables and the unit of comparison are identified. Quantitative data is then adjusted (i.e., interpreted) based on differences between each comparable sale property and the subject. While both traditional valuation and appraisal valuation modeling employ all three components, the difference lies is in the scope of the analysis. Only appraisal valuation modeling can effectively use all of the available market data.

What phenomena cannot be analyzed? Obvious examples include real estate activity of a confidential nature, where the data is concealed. In such cases, market- or industry-derived factors can be used, as long as the appraiser makes it clear in the appraisal that specific property data is unavailable. When standard factors or comparable properties are not available, an appraiser may not be able to perform the appraisal assignment at all.

Figure 2.1 **Statistical Analysis**

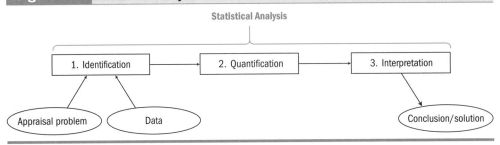

Identification

Identifying what particular real estate phenomenon (or variable) is of interest depends on the purpose of the appraisal analysis. The goal could be one of the following:

- To specify important elements of comparison that affect overall value
- To value a group of properties in a given area
- To create a broad valuation model
- To "mark to market" (i.e., value) a portfolio of real property, financial securities, or derivatives
- To estimate risk

The goal of the analysis determines what type of valuation strategy should be employed. For example, an appraiser should not create a regression model with numerous variables to value residential properties if the market that determines those values uses a smaller set of variables. The presence of a swimming pool may theoretically increase property value, but that increase can be affected by other factors, such as location (e.g., if the property is in Alaska or in Arizona) or whether a pool is a typical upgrade feature in that neighborhood. If there are no sale properties with swimming pools, then the appraiser cannot adequately analyze its impact on property values anyway. If most properties have swimming pools, such as in upscale neighborhoods in warm climates, then it may be impossible to separate the impact that factor has because it is associated with all large, high-quality homes.

Identification is important not only in analyzing the overall valuation problem correctly but also in choosing the specific variables that will be analyzed. It sets the stage for the entire appraisal valuation analysis. It is not limited to the set of variables chosen; identification includes all preliminary steps in the valuation process.

Quantification

Once the scope of the appraisal and all relevant variables are identified, measuring them and calculating their impact allows the appraiser to quantify their effect. Calculating the influence of a phenomenon links the identification and interpretive steps in an analysis.

The actual calculation of a variable's influence can be the easiest step in statistical analysis, depending on the appraiser's toolbox. If the appraiser is limited to a pad of paper and a financial calculator, the analysis can take hours or even days. It can also limit the scope of analysis. When appraisers use software such as electronic spreadsheets (Microsoft Excel, Lotus, Corel Quattro Pro) or databases (Access, dBase), the quantification step can take much less time. Specialized analytical software packages, such as SPSS and MiniTab, offer the best package for data analysis and are highly recommended.

To measure data correctly the appraiser must understand

- Some basic concepts behind the data
- The types of data
- Limitations of the data
- Some considerations about the source of the data

This analytical step produces *output*. It is through the interpretation of this output that the appraiser applies appraisal theory to solve the appraisal problem at hand.

Interpretation

The primary objective of this final step is to ensure that the output from the analysis makes appraisal sense, but, if the process includes statistical applications, the appraiser needs to understand the statistical analysis that drove the measurement process as well. This requires basic competence (the goal of this book) and must be presented in a manner that the client can understand. It does not require the appraiser to have graduate-level education in statistics, but it does require basic competence concerning the correct interpretation of any analytical output.

This step essentially concludes the analytical process by evaluating all output from an appraisal perspective. The appraiser must apply valuation theory to interpret this output correctly. This theory is not part of a new branch of appraisal but rather a restatement of existing and accepted standards of appraisal practice.

data
In statistics, information or facts, usually in numerical form, that can be classified by qualitative characteristics in ratios, by size in frequency distributions, or by time in time series or regression analysis.

information
In statistics, any data that throws light on the estimated parameter, measured by the Fisher Information number. As the number increases, the variance of the estimate decreases (reliability increases).

Note: These definitions and those on the following pages of this chapter are quoted from *The Dictionary of Real Estate Appraisal*, 4th ed. (Chicago: Appraisal Institute, 2002).

Output is simply the product of your analysis. It can be as crude as a handwritten adjustment grid or as sophisticated as graphical output from a statistical software package such as SPSS or MiniTab.

Some Important Terms and Concepts

Population and Sample

A *sample* is usually a subset of the larger, complete set of data points making up the *population*. An understanding of these two related terms is important when framing a statistical analysis because there are some minor differences in the calculations of certain descriptive statistical measures, such as the average and standard deviation. In most circumstances, market data such as a set of sales data can be considered a representative sample of the larger population of a certain class of property, both sold and unsold. The subject property is included in this population as well. Framing the analysis properly allows for the correct interpretation of the relationship between market data (sample) and the subject (part of the population).

Statistical analysis is often concerned with sample data. For example, pollsters cannot ask everyone in the nation what their favorite television programs are. They can, however, ask a sample of persons who watch television that question and then make a statistical inference about the entire population. This inferential step is based on what is known about the sample and how that sample reflects the population. A sample that is very similar to the population would tend to be more reliable than one that does not reflect the population accurately. Determining the similarity of a real estate sample involves appraisal judgment and common sense. Both statistical theory and real-world considerations, such as time frames, budgets, and the other resources available, influence this judgment process.

Populations involve all items in a group. The familiar example of television ratings includes all television viewers during a particular time frame. Samples then are subsets of the population. The relationship of a sample to the population is very important because it can determine whether the analyst correctly answers the question or problem. For example, should the population be all television viewers who actually watch television, or should it be those who could watch television (i.e., everyone who owns one or more TVs)? Or maybe the population is all households in the United States.

Variable

A *variable* is the term used for a property attribute that may take on different values across different properties. For example, the parking ratio of a shopping cen-

Figure 2.2 Population and Samples

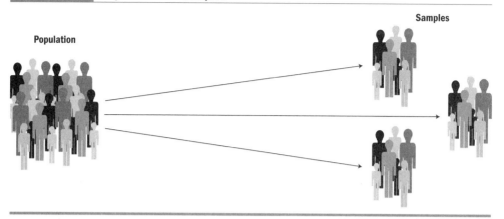

ter is a variable because different centers have different parking ratios. One center may have a parking ratio of 4.5 spaces per thousand square feet of gross leasable area, while another center has a ratio of 5.2 spaces per thousand. The sale price is another variable because different properties sell for different prices.

When performing any valuation analysis, an important concept involves independent and dependent variables, as diagramed in Figure 2.3. Generally, the appraiser is interested in deriving an estimate of the value of the dependent variable from the independent variables. This is true whether the appraisal is a traditional appraisal or one that employs a statistical valuation model. Although causation between variables is technically not provable, the association between these variable sets must make appraisal sense and must be explained in those terms.

For example, a single-family residence with a greater total living area (an independent variable) would be expected to result in greater sale price (the dependent variable) than a smaller home. The

variable
An item of observation that can assume various values, for example, square feet, sale prices, or sales ratios. Variables are commonly described using measures of central tendency and dispersion.

dependent variable
The variable that may be or is believed to be predicted by or caused by independent variables; response, explained, or predicted variable.

Value is a variable that is typically not part of the appraisal modeling process, although it is often the goal of the appraisal to conclude an estimate of market value for the subject property. The terms *market value* and *sale price* (of comparable properties) are commonly used interchangeably, indicating the importance of correctly defining *value* in the appraisal. Sale price in effect becomes a proxy for market value.

Figure 2.3 Independent and Dependent Variables

Dependent Variables	Independent Variables
Sale price	Improved area
or	Age
Rental rate	Land area
or	Condition
Cap rate	Quality
or	Parking
Cost factor	Fireplaces
	Office finish
	Stories

appraiser needs to explain such a relationship whether performing a traditional appraisal with a manual adjustment grid or using a statistically based appraisal valuation model. In both instances, the relationship between the dependent variable and the independent variables is the same.

Categories of Data

There are four different categories of data:

1. Nominal (qualitative)
2. Ordinal (qualitative)
3. Interval (quantitative)
4. Ratio (quantitative)

Each of these categories is relevant in the description and analysis of data. Each is a measurement of a sort, and each signifies a different level of measurement. These levels are useful in determining which statistical procedures are appropriate to use in analyzing the data.

Nominal Data

Nominal data uses numbers or labels to categorize and classify information. Examples include construction type, roof material, or other variables that identify a property but do not quantify it. While these data points describe the property, they do not lend themselves to mathematical operations. It is, for example, impossible to add two of these data points together (e.g., "metal construction" plus "precast concrete construction" is mathematically meaningless). Even though nominal data points cannot be used in their raw form in mathematical operations, they can be used to define the number of observations that fall into a given category. For instance, in descriptive statistics such as frequency distributions or percentages, it would be useful to know the number of occurrences within a neighborhood defined as a nominal variable.

Membership in a particular group does not imply any quantifiable difference from any other groups. In other words, a nominal variable simply names a phenomenon. (The word *nominal* derives from the Latin root *nomen*, which means name.) A generic example is a variable for location based on two neighborhoods, labeled 1 and 2. There is no inherent numerical difference between these values; the numbers simply distinguish whether a property is located in one neighborhood or the other. The appraiser could have just as easily used the letters A and B to label these neighborhoods.

Limitations of Data

The type of data chosen limits the type of statistical techniques that can be used in analysis. Care must always be exercised to ensure that the proper data type is used in the decision-making process.

Examples of Four Types of Data			
Qualitative		**Quantitative**	
Nominal data	**Ordinal data**	**Interval data**	**Ratio data**
• Census tract	• Quality	• Time (year of construction)	• Sale price
• Type of building	• Condition		• Size of building
• Type of zoning	• Utility		• Age of building
			• Size of parcel
			• Number of stories

Some additional examples of nominal variables used in real estate appraisal include

• Type of shopping center–e.g., neighborhood center, community center, regional mall, power center, specialty center, lifestyle center, entertainment retail center, or discount center

• Type of industrial property–e.g., warehouse, flex, R&D

• Type of single-family residence–e.g., ranch, two-story, bilevel

Ordinal Data

Data described as *ordinal* is organized by rankings–e.g., first, second, third. Ordinal data can be useful when it is difficult to obtain more specific information about the phenomenon being described. Ordinal data contains more information than nominal data but is still limited and not used in many statistical techniques.

Ordinal data represents a measure of order within a hierarchy. Examples include any comparison of a higher scale point to a lower scale point. The most frequent use of this type of data in real estate appraisal includes categories such as the construction quality or condition of a given property. An example of construction quality could be demonstrated as follows:

1. Excellent
2. Very good
3. Good
4. Average
5. Fair
6. Poor

It is important to note that the distance between the points is unspecified. The appraiser would still have some questions about the differences between

ordinal variable
A variable based on a ranked order of data, such as a measurement of quality of construction based on a scale of 1 through 5. This type of variable provides more information than nominal data, although it is more limited than interval or ratio variables since the rankings themselves do not provide any information concerning the distance between each ranking. In other words, a ranking variable for quality does not imply that a score of 4 is twice as good as a score of 2; the correct interpretation would be that the score of 4 is two levels above the score of 2.

the scores. For example, how much better is a "good" property than an "average" property? Is the spacing between the categories consistent? The important concept to understand is that ordinal data incorporates rankings, though the distance between scale values is undefined. Each ranking should be in sequence, e.g., lesser to greater.

Treating ordinal level data as if it were ratio- or interval-level data can create problems. For example, assume that a data set representing construction quality has four levels: excellent, good, average, and poor, coded respectively as 1, 2, 3, and 4. If this variable is used in a regression model "as is," the model will treat the spacing between each level as equal, developing adjustments of equal amounts between each level of quality. The actual sales data may show something entirely different. Excellent properties may be $25,000 above good properties, while good properties may only be $3,000 above average properties. The scale by itself does not reveal the difference in value between each level in the hierarchy established for the variable **Property Condition**.

The problem with spacing may be evident whenever there are more than two categories within the variable. Sometimes methods such as paired sales analysis can be used to create separate values for each quality level, but more advanced procedures such as regression analysis are better ways to treat this problem. Ordered data can be used as long as the distance between variable values is not taken "as is."

Additional examples of ordinal data germane to real estate would include

- Socioeconomic income classes in a community— e.g., poverty-level, low-income, middle-income, upper-income, affluent
- Class of office buildings—e.g., Class A, Class B, Class C

Interval and Ratio Data

Interval variables have quantifiable differences between each value. An example is the year of construction, where the number of years between two values represents the numeric difference between each year. A property with a year of construction of 1964 is 30 years older than a property with a year of construction of 1994. These variables have a meaningful scale yet no absolute zero point on the scale. A non-real estate example of an interval variable is temperature. On the Fahrenheit scale, a temperature reading of 60 degrees is clearly 30 degrees warmer

Think of *order* when you see the *ordinal data* classification.

Nominal and ordinal data are also known as *categorical data* because the primary information derived pertains to group membership—for example, if the property is part of Subdivision A or Subdivision B. These categories are either unranked (nominal) or ranked (ordinal).

than a temperature of 30 degrees, but it is not twice as warm since 0 degrees is simply a benchmark and does not signify the complete absence of heat.

For appraisers, the **Year of Construction** variable is the most relevant interval-level variable. In valuation modeling, appraisers should change the **Year of Construction (YOC)** variable to an age-equivalent variable. Using an **Age** variable, which is a *ratio-level variable*, allows for adjustments to be interpreted more easily. The following valuation equation was derived from a simple regression model for industrial properties, using the year of construction instead of age:

sale price = -$17,000,000 + $24.99 (bldg. sq. ft.) + $313,884 (land acres)
    + $8,132 (YOC)
sale price = -$17,000,000 + $24.99 (100,000) + $313,884 (3)
    + $8,132 (1994) = $2,655,860

While certainly "correct" in a statistical sense, using the **YOC** variable results in a large negative constant value and a large coefficient value for the **YOC** adjustment. Replacing **YOC** with the age of the improvements changes the valuation equation to the following:

sale price = $703,472 + $24.99 (bldg. sq. ft.) + $313,884 (land acres)
    − $8,132 (effective age)
sale price = $703,472 + $24.99 (100,000) + $313,884 (3)
    − $8,132 (10) = $2,655,860

Mathematically, both equations yield the same value for the subject property. The statistics measuring the accuracy of the model are also the same, but the coefficient value for **Age** is now easily interpreted and could be used directly in any valuation adjustment. The constant (in orange in the revised equation) measures the base value of the valuation equation prior to adjustments. Note that after **YOC** is replaced by the ratio-level **Age** variable, the constant is smaller and more in line with the coefficient values.

Ratio variables are like interval variables, but the scale has an identifiable absolute zero point for the attribute. If you transform the **Year of Construction** to **Age**, then you have transformed an interval-level variable to a ratio-level data because **Age** has a zero point. Most descriptive statistical calculations require interval or ratio variables.

Both interval and ratio data involve measurable distance between numbers. Thus comparisons can be made between one distinct data point and the next. Ratio data differs from interval-level data because its ratios are meaningful. Dividing a ratio-level variable by another yields a meaningful ratio statistic; this cannot be done with interval-level data.

interval variable
A variable based on the actual numeric value of the data itself, i.e., the intervals between the values of the variable are equally spaced. A variable such as annual income, measured in dollars, contains all of the attributes of nominal and ordinal data, but it also possesses meaning in terms of the differences between values. For example, the difference in annual income between properties with incomes of $150,000 and $175,000 is the same as the difference between properties with incomes of $200,000 and $225,000.

ratio-level variable
A variable based on the actual numeric value of the data itself, like an interval variable but in addition the calibrations that allow the numerical difference between values to be measured are based on a natural or true zero point.

If you divide 1964 by 1994, you get 0.98. If you transform these interval variables into **Age** (a ratio variable) using 2003 as the current year, you get 39/9, or 4.3. The first ratio is meaningless; the second ratio indicates that a building with an age of 39 years is 4.3 times as old as one that is 9 years old.

Ratio data incorporates both the concept of a zero point and the nature of interval data, providing a ranking of data that can be used numerically in the data analysis process. Ratio measurement is based on an ordered series of number rankings beginning with zero. The relationship between the number rankings indicates the absolute value of the data, such that a retail building with a sale price of $1 million costs twice as much as a retail building with a sale price of $500,000.

For quantitative data (both interval and ratio data), the data value itself provides explicit information in that equal differences have equal meaning. There is always a unit of measure involved, such as square feet, acres, roof pitch, or number of apartment units. Most data of this type is *continuous* in that it can always be measured more and more precisely, like square feet of area (e.g., 423.6 square feet). Or it can be *discrete*, like the number of apartment bedrooms (1, 2, or 3) or number of baths (1, $1\frac{1}{2}$, 2, $2\frac{1}{2}$, etc.). With all quantitative data, either continuous or discrete, the intervals between the values are quantitatively meaningful.

As noted, ratio data does allow multiplication and division (as well as adding and subtracting). For example, a home that has 2,200 square feet of GLA is 83% larger than a home that has 1,200 square feet. The difference between the sizes of the two homes, 1,000 square feet, has real meaning that can be measured and interpreted as a percentage difference (i.e., the difference in size divided by the size of the smaller house). On the other hand, a home with a construction quality rating of excellent and an ordinal value rating of 2 is not necessarily twice as "well-constructed" as a home with a construction quality rating of average that corresponds to a rating of 1.

The bottom-line difference between qualitative data and quantitative data is that the latter yields more *information*. Statistical analysis that uses interval or ratio data yields more information than analyses using just nominal- or ordinal-level data.

With the lion's share of statistical theory in this book now out of the way, the stage is set for a discussion of the initial steps of practical data analysis, which is covered in the next chapter.

Equation Mechanics

Mathematical equations are used all the time by appraisers. They are used in the cost approach to quantify depreciation, in the income capitalization approach to adjust market-based rental data, and in the sales comparison approach to adjust comparable sale properties to the subject. As a simple definition, an equation relates the values on one side of an equals sign to the other.

The equations elementary school students encounter are simple arithmetic, in which all of the terms are numeric, such as

$$2 + 2 = 4$$
$$2 \times 3 = 6$$

When students hit algebra later in junior high or high school, equations get a little more complex, such as

$$2a + 4 = 6$$

Algebra has special rules—e.g., first multiply 2 by the value of the variable a, and then add 4. It also has tricks every student learns, such as subtracting 4 from both sides of this equation to make it a little more straightforward.

$$2a + 4 \, (-4) = 6 \, (-4)$$
$$2a + 0 = 2$$

Dividing each side of the simpler equation $2a = 2$ by 2 results in a new equation, $a = 1$. The original equation, $2a + 4 = 6$, has been "solved" for the variable a.

For students of calculus or introductory statistics, mathematical gymnastics like this are combined to develop and solve complex formulas. But all of this mathematics is still based on the basic equation form.

In appraisal, the basic equation usually involves market variables on one side of the equals sign and a market value on the other side. The value side usually refers to the subject of the appraisal. In appraisal, equations can be simple or complex:

Simple: Market Value = Replacement Cost New – Depreciation
Complex: Market Value = $B_0 \times$ Lotsize^{B1} + $B_2 \times$ Views

In both of the examples above, the two sides of the equations are related by an equals sign (hence the term *equation*). One side equates to the other.

The term *linear equation* refers to how change on one side of the equation affects the other. In most cases, a change on the attribute side of an appraisal equation results in a predictable change on the value side. The rate of change, the coefficient, is a fixed amount (think of a whole dollar adjustment to the price of a comparable sale). If the variables in an equation have a linear relationship, such as **House Size** and **Market Value** in the following equation:

Market Value = House Size × Price per Square Foot

then graphing the two variables would result in a straight line (think of the *line* in *linear*) because each unit increase in square footage raises the sale price by a fixed amount (i.e., $50 per square foot in the example illustrated by the graph). This type of equation is theoretical because house size does not perfectly predict house value in the real world.

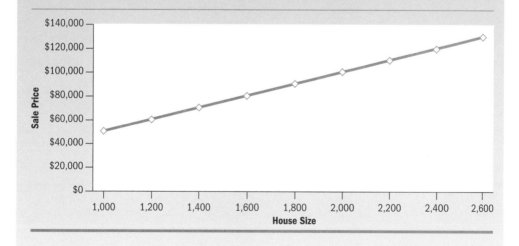

A slightly more complex (and more realistic) linear equation involves more than one variable on the attribute side and a constant value, as shown in the following equation:

Market Value = Constant + (House Size × Price per Square Foot) − (Age × Depreciation per Year)
$70,000 = $30,000 + (1,500 × $60) − (25 × $2,000)

In the example above, the valuation equation is based on two variables (**House Size** and **Age**) as well as a constant term of $30,000.

What is the constant? Technically, the constant is the residual value when all of the variables equal zero. According to most real estate modeling practitioners, the constant does not equate to the residual land value, although at first glance this would appear to be an obvious interpretation–i.e., there are no improvements present on the vacant land, so all the attribute values are zero and the constant must be the value of the land, the only thing left for the equation to value. There are two reasons to reconsider that interpretation:

1. Often a valuation equation includes a variable for land size because the size of a lot or parcel can affect market value. If the size or some other characteristic of the site is one of the variables in the valuation equation, then the land value cannot be explained solely by the constant.
2. Even if the variable portion of the equation does not have land variables, the constant value could not be the residual value associated with the land because there is often a gap between a hypothetical property with a size of zero and the smallest actual property.

The following simple example, using the variable **Gross Living Area** to predict the market value, illustrates this gap:

Sale #	Market Value	=	Constant	+	GLA	×	Coefficient
1	$100,000	=	$25,000	+	1,500 sq. ft.	×	$50 per sq. ft.
2	$75,000	=	$25,000	+	1,000 sq. ft.	×	$50 per sq. ft.
3	$85,000	=	$25,000	+	1,200 sq. ft.	×	$50 per sq. ft.
4	$150,000	=	$25,000	+	2,500 sq. ft.	×	$50 per sq. ft.
5	$125,000	=	$25,000	+	2,000 sq. ft.	×	$50 per sq. ft.

Even assuming that gross living area "explains" most of the value in the equation, remember that the constant holds for homes of any size. If the house has 2,500 square feet, the constant is $25,000. If another house has 1,000 square feet, the constant in the valuation equation is still $25,000. The "gap" referred to earlier represents the distance between the hypothetical situation (GLA = 0) and the smallest house in the data set, which is 1,000 square feet. Although house size could be smaller (between 0 and 1,000 square feet), this range is not normally seen. Common sense dictates that houses cannot have a gross living area of merely 25, 75, or even 300 square feet.

Another reason that the constant does not represent the land value is that it does not make appraisal sense. At $150,000, the land value would account for 17% of the total property value, while at $75,000, the land value would account for 33% of the total value, all in the same neighborhood. Developers and sellers of real estate never value land in this manner.

The basic form for the equations used in most real estate valuation models is the linear form. This form will be used in the statistical analyses presented in this book, including the regression modeling (hence the term linear regression). Use the following as a guide:

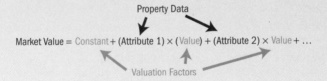

Property Data

Market Value = Constant + (Attribute 1) × (Value) + (Attribute 2) × Value + ...

Valuation Factors

The analyst provides the property data while the regression model (in this example) provides the numeric valuation factors. Together, property data and valuation factors form the basic valuation equation. The specific variables and factors will differ from model to model, but the equation mechanics remain the same. One side equals the other.

CHAPTER 3

Data Exploration

"Every journey begins with a single step."

−ancient proverb

Statistical analysis is a broad discipline. Untrained analysts can feel overwhelmed when considering the range of statistical applications available. The data itself can be overwhelming in terms of numbers and sources. Developing observations from the raw data can be impossible when a data set has more than 30 sales. The mind despairs and tunes out that much data, treating it as noise.

At this point many will attempt to pull out five or six sales, literally by sight, and deem them comparable, leaving the remaining data (and most of the market) out of the analysis. Some may try to back into the analysis by selecting those few comparable sales and then developing a bridge to the other data. If indeed the mind cannot process more than a few comparable properties with a few adjustments, then true appraisal professionals must adapt to the data. There are specific methods that must be used when examining market data of this magnitude.

This chapter focuses on basic exploratory data analysis (EDA), the first step in any valuation analysis. The next chapter will cover *descriptive statistics* using variables that describe the subject property and comparable market data, such as the number of bathrooms, location, and condition. Later chapters will deal with applications that relate market data to the subject. Such *inferential analysis* uses statistical methods that measure the relationships between variables such as the sale price and property attributes like gross building area, gross living area, and land size.

The data set used in the next several chapters is a set of industrial sales. The same statistical rules and recommendations apply whether an appraiser is analyzing a residential data set or a collection of rental comparables. Any exceptions to the AVM methods used in the examples will be indicated. While some steps can be omitted (depending on spe-

While the HP-12C (and almost any financial calculator) is a good financial analysis tool, the authors maintain that it is similar to using vintage airplane technology in the jet age.

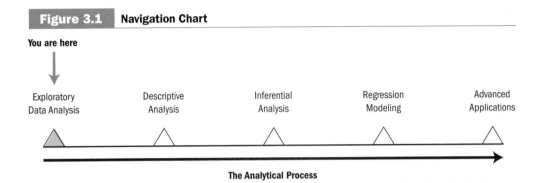

Figure 3.1 Navigation Chart

You are here

Exploratory Data Analysis — Descriptive Analysis — Inferential Analysis — Regression Modeling — Advanced Applications

The Analytical Process

cific data issues), most should be followed in the sequence presented.

As the navigation chart (Figure 3.1) indicates, exploratory data analysis is always the first step because appraisers must effectively evaluate the format and content of their data set before using it in the valuation process. In addition, under USPAP appraisers must convey appropriate information about the market data used in the appraisal process to the intended users of their appraisals.

Frame Your Analysis

A critical step in any analysis is setting up the correct statistical framework, a process that is synonymous with correctly defining the appraisal problem in the valuation process. Think of the process as stepping back from an appraisal problem and asking, "Does this really make sense?" To properly frame an analysis, an appraiser must be comfortable with the important terms *population* and *sample.*

In real estate analysis, the relationship between sample and population is especially important. Does the readily accessible data on single-family home sales in a neighborhood reflect the population of all single-family home sales, or does it represent a sample of sales? Here the scope of work and appraisal judgment can provide the answers. If the scope of the assignment is to value a property that is for sale or that has recently been sold on the open market, then the sales data reflects the entire population of interest, and the subject property is included in that population. If the subject is an unsold single-family home, then the sales data is a sample of the total population of homes in that neighborhood.

In either case the same questions must be answered:

- Are the sales comparable to the subject(s)?

- Are the sales comparable to one another?
- Are there any exogenous (i.e., outside) factors affecting the sales data?
- Are there any internal factors affecting the sales data?

The basic question of comparability is always important in an appraisal because the judgment of comparability links the market data and the subject property. In mass appraisal, where every home would be valued based on the sales data, the question is whether the sales data reflects the important attributes of the population of all single-family homes. In a single-property appraisal, the focus then becomes one property, but the question of comparability remains the same. Does the data compare reasonably to the subject?

An aside is necessary at this point. Sampling theory assumes a random selection process in most instances. In this example, the assumption would be that all single-family homes in the neighborhood had the same chance of being sold. While this appears to be a faulty assumption, since the owners of each property do not randomly place their homes on the market for sale, a simple modification makes it more applicable. The decision to place a property on the market involves a multitude of factors, including consumer preferences, employment trends, income trends, societal trends, governmental trends (e.g., the construction of a new freeway through a housing development), and environmental trends. Note the similarity between these considerations and the regional/market analysis required in every appraisal. As long as the same factors influencing the desire to sell hold across *all* properties in a defined neighborhood, then it is generally safe to assume that the sales population or sample would behave as if it had been selected at random.

The assumption of randomness affects the comparability of sample data and the subject property. Bias can render the comparison misleading; this can be due to a systematic bias in the data or poor data selection. An example of the former would be a sales data set dominated by homes with golf course frontage used to value a home *not* on a golf course. An example of the latter would be a sales data set obtained from a local multiple listing service that includes sales data that is incomplete or incorrect. Correcting the former could include excluding sales

Random samples assume that all items in the population had the same chance to be selected. In other words, the *probability* of being selected is the same for all items in the population.

A Note on Verification

Continually verifying market transactions and data is critical for single-property appraisers, and exploratory data analysis can help identify suspected problem data. For example, assume that 400 industrial sales are selected to value a single industrial building. Market stratification reduces this to 50 comparable sales. While ideally *all* 50 of these sales would be confirmed by the appraiser, an alternative strategy would be to use exploratory data analysis to identify sales that *must* be personally confirmed.

Assume that all 50 sales are arrayed by sale price per square foot, with 49 of the sales ranging from $15 to $39 per square foot. The fiftieth sale is $300 per square foot. The appraiser could then verify whether this outlier sale is a mistake or an accurately recorded sale albeit with an extreme value. The price per square foot could be in error (i.e., coded as $300 per square foot instead of the correct $30 per square foot), or the property could be incorrectly included in the industrial sales data set (e.g., it is really an office building). Outliers generally include mistakes or mislabeling and should typically be removed from the data set. Extreme values generally include correctly coded and identified data.

> Appraisers can also use other verification sources, such as vendor-supplied or county assessment verification, to augment the verification of large market data sets.

If the industrial property is truly $300 per square foot, the appraiser should ask if it should remain in the data set. This would depend on the subject property and issues of comparability, and it is a matter of appraisal judgment. If the inclusion of this sale skews the analysis significantly without providing much information, then the answer is obvious—exclude it. On the other hand, extreme values can provide important market information about how the market values properties at the extreme. As always, appraisers need to understand that extreme values affect the statistical measures that describe their data.

with golf course frontage or accounting for the bias, perhaps by coding golf course and off-golf course sales separately. Correcting the latter problem would include proper market verification and sales from other sources, such as the county assessor.

If the market data's comparability is acceptable, then the appraiser can proceed with the process of inferring a relationship between that market data and the subject. If the market data does not compare overall to the subject, then the market data must be sliced and diced into smaller subsets that *are* comparable. If that does not work, then the appraiser needs to consider whether the market data is correctly defined. A new set of market data may be needed to complete the analysis.

Stratification

The process of dividing the market data into more comparable subsets is known as *stratification*. Market data can be stratified based on one or more attributes, such as effective age, size, and location. A simple stratification of the single-family home sales data set would be to include only ranch-style homes (assuming the subject property is a ranch-style home). A more complex stratification would be to select only ranch-style homes constructed between 1970 and 1980 with 1,000 to 2,000 square feet of gross living area. Stratifying can make market data more focused and ultimately more comparable to the subject.

> Stratified samples are often used for sales data in neighborhoods with a lot of variation. They are also used in commercial appraisal, where the market data tends to cross property use classes.

The other major questions at the framing stage have already been answered. Stratifying data can help counter any biases in market data. For example, if the sales data consists primarily of two-story homes on an adjacent golf course but the subject property is a ranch-style home away from the golf course, then stratification can help exclude sales that are perhaps not very comparable. The internal consistency of the market data could be addressed by including or excluding data based on the same set of stratification factors. The data could be stratified by time, if more appropriate sales are clustered at the beginning, middle, or end of the sale period. This may also provide important market information about the subject property. If all of the recent sales occurred in a neighborhood away from a proposed highway corridor, then the subject property (assuming it is along this corridor) suffers from a degree of external obsolescence. Appraisal judgment is important at this preliminary stage of the analysis to help address these issues.

Stratification is already used by most appraisers in the manual selection of comparable market data. The same considerations need to be addressed when developing an appraisal valuation model, with one important caveat. Since statistical procedures require a minimum number of data points to be effective, overstratification can render the supply of market data so small that no analysis can be performed.

Sometimes market data *is* scarce and, if that is the case, the appraiser must consider using that very small data set with its inherent limitations or expanding the scope of analysis. If there are only three truly comparable sales in the residential neighborhood example, then the appraiser must decide whether to use only those sales or to include other sales of similar properties from similar neighborhoods. This decision must be described or summarized in the appraisal report as well. In this case, the additional complication of adding a new neighborhood to the data set could be outweighed by the market information gained from the additional data. For example, if all three sales in the neighborhood were over one year old, then including other sales would probably be supportable. If the three sales resulted from the stratification, then the stratification framework could also be modified. All of this requires thorough knowledge of the market. Notice that little of the analysis so far has relied solely on sophisticated statistical expertise.

Exploratory Data Analysis

The First Step

Exploratory data analysis is simply that: the preliminary examination and mapping of the data set. This step is essential because it determines whether the data set is complete or needs further refinement through editing or recoding. The first check is of the completeness of the data set. In other words, are the variables sufficient to value the subject? Are there any missing variables from the data set? If so, can they be added now or can the analysis proceed without them? Every appraiser should already be asking these questions when they are analyzing data.

Since at this point the data is not being manipulated, the appraiser can simply look at the data in a spreadsheet or table to determine whether key variables that should be included in the valuation analysis are missing. For example, in a residential valuation data set, the omission of a variable for **Fireplace** is less critical than one for **Total Living Area**. Or, in examining Table 3.1 (an industrial data set of 450 sale properties with the first 25 shown) an appraiser would have to question the completeness of the data if a variable for the number of **Overhead Doors** was included but the **Year of Construction** (or **Age**) was not. Note that these conclusions are based on appraisal judgment rather than statistical judgment.

If the appraiser determines that the variables in the data set are sufficient, the next step concerns the data itself. Are there any missing values, extreme values, or values that appear to be incorrect? In Table 3.1, the appraisers excluded any sale variable that had missing or unexplained extreme values. Often this type of verification does not require field inspections. An industrial sale with an age of 300 years is probably incorrect, as would be an industrial sale with a negative total improved area.

Using arrayed data provides an easy method to check for extreme, missing, or incorrect values. This task can be performed manually with a spreadsheet or using a statistical package such as SPSS or Minitab. Appraisers can use a handheld calculator but, again, using a spreadsheet or statistical software package is strongly recommended. Arraying and editing the variables in Table 3.1 took approximately five minutes using Excel. The table format of spreadsheets makes this process easy and quick. The sale file began with over 700 sales from the Denver market; once data was edited for missing, extreme, or incorrect values, the sales data set was reduced to 450 sales.

The goal of exploratory data analysis (EDA) is to evaluate the adequacy of the scope of the data. For the appraiser, it is a systematic way to array data for the purpose of editing it. The goal here is not to provide a framework to value the subject; instead, it is a preliminary step to prepare data for statistical analysis and ultimately for appraisal modeling.

The process of sorting data by variable value is termed *arraying* the data. Simply put, it is rearranging data in either descending or ascending order based on one or more variables. Its purpose is not only to edit data but also to give appraisers an indication as to the range of data.

Table 3.1 — Industrial Sales Data Set (1998–2001)

Sale Date	Sale Price	Imp. Area	Age	Land Area	Construction	Property Use
4/5/2001	$710,000	12,400	47	0.2873	Concrete block	Multitenant industrial building
11/30/2000	$328,800	8,064	29	0.321	Precast concrete	Single-tenant industrial building
5/26/2000	$625,000	17,787	19	0.879	Metal	Single-tenant industrial building
8/20/2001	$250,000	2,300	2	0.3444	Concrete block	Single-tenant industrial building
11/9/1999	$775,000	10,080	1	0.987	Concrete tilt-up	Single-tenant industrial building
7/18/2000	$8,251,500	229,200	1	11.8554	Poured concrete	Single-tenant industrial building
6/18/2001	$540,000	18,540	83	0.621	Structural brick	Single-tenant industrial building
11/13/2000	$2,000,000	83,100	47	5.7889	Metal	Single-tenant industrial building
9/8/2000	$2,450,000	121,450	40	4.726	Metal	Multitenant industrial building
10/9/2001	$300,000	4,430	22	0.301	Metal	Multitenant industrial building
1/18/2001	$5,500,000	200,000	16	12.354	Concrete tilt-up	Warehouse/distribution
9/1/1999	$780,000	29,044	42	0.577	Concrete block	Single-tenant industrial building
11/17/2000	$300,000	4,970	40	0.287	Structural brick	Food processing plant
7/12/1999	$700,000	14,000	4	2.14	Metal	Single-tenant industrial building
6/18/1998	$545,000	25,466	48	0.6095	Mixed construction	Multitenant industrial building
6/28/2001	$2,750,000	100,160	26	5.167	Precast concrete	Single-tenant industrial building
12/6/1999	$1,810,000	45,000	13	4.005	Concrete tilt-up	Single-tenant industrial building
4/28/2000	$1,890,400	45,000	14	2.873	Concrete tilt-up	Single-tenant industrial building
8/18/2000	$4,400,000	69,190	3	16.52	Mixed construction	Single-tenant industrial building
9/1/1998	$275,000	2,880	38	2.45	Metal	Industrial shop
11/6/1998	$320,000	4,000	27	4.7	Concrete block	Industrial zoned garage/auto repair
4/27/1999	$1,075,000	20,772	23	5.76	Metal	Single-tenant industrial building
6/28/2000	$2,800,000	63,080	22	4.39	Poured concrete	Multitenant industrial building
5/20/1999	$565,000	10,000	15	2.175	Metal	Multitenant industrial building
11/26/2001	$4,800,000	153,000	28	6.2913	Structural brick	Single-tenant industrial building

Arraying the data also provides the appraiser with a systematic look at the data. Even with extremely large data sets of 450 industrial sales, the appraiser can easily see the range of data between the smallest and largest values. This is similar to manual methods of selecting comparable sales, albeit using a more systematic and demonstrable method. In Table 3.2, samples of two variables from the industrial sales data set are presented as first raw and then arrayed data.

In Table 3.2 the sale date indicates the distribution of sales over the four-year sale period represented by these 18 sales. The range of sale prices is also clearly indicated when the data is arrayed by that variable. Arraying data conveys information about the range and distribution of the data that the appraiser can recognize prior to any formal descriptive analysis.

The reader can already determine that a manual manipulation of a large data set can be complex and time-consuming. Sorting and editing hundreds of sales on cards or other manual tracking systems quickly becomes self-defeating, and it is something a handy financial calculator cannot fix.

Table 3.2	Unsorted and Arrayed Data Sets			
Sale Date			**Sale Price**	
Unsorted	Arrayed		Unsorted	Arrayed
4/5/2001	4/2/1998		$710,000	$250,000
11/30/2000	6/18/1998		$328,800	$300,000
5/26/2000	7/12/1999		$625,000	$300,000
4/2/1998	9/1/1999		$335,000	$328,800
8/20/2001	11/9/1999		$250,000	$335,000
11/9/1999	5/26/2000		$775,000	$376,000
7/18/2000	7/18/2000		$8,251,500	$540,000
9/21/2000	9/8/2000		$376,000	$545,000
6/18/2001	9/21/2000		$540,000	$625,000
11/13/2000	11/13/2000		$2,000,000	$700,000
9/8/2000	11/17/2000		$2,450,000	$710,000
10/9/2001	11/30/2000		$300,000	$775,000
1/18/2001	1/18/2001		$5,500,000	$780,000
9/1/1999	4/5/2001		$780,000	$2,000,000
11/17/2000	6/18/2001		$300,000	$2,450,000
7/12/1999	6/28/2001		$700,000	$2,750,000
6/18/1998	8/20/2001		$545,000	$5,500,000
6/28/2001	10/9/2001		$2,750,000	$8,251,500

At this point the appraiser can focus the selection process based on property attributes. When appraising an office building, the appraiser may decide that sale properties ranging from 10,000 to 20,000 square feet in total improved area are the most comparable. Manipulating the data at this stage restricts the analysis, but this restriction may provide for a more focused appraisal analysis. Of course, the appraiser needs to consider the consequences of limiting the scope of analysis. Restricting sales data to office properties between 10,000 and 20,000 square feet may result in too few sales for supportable and persuasive statistical analysis. It may also exclude sales literally across the street from the subject that do not meet the selection criteria.

The goal of these initial steps is to pare raw market data down into a data set that is comparable to the subject. Arraying the raw data and checking for missing, extreme, or incorrect values prepares the data for a systematic descriptive analysis, which is discussed in the next chapter.

Arrays use ordinal, interval, and ratio-level data. You cannot array a nominal variable.

CHAPTER 4

80,057.76   2,005,625.84   1,008,560.72
1,252,440.09   954,166.78   515,468.19
6,784,550.35   7   308.62   1,500,078.11   71,624.16
770,122.46   17.80   40,0?3.25
954,876.19   64.35
1,605,470.   24.67   16°
82,441.   84.29
848,627.07   4,532.19
12,558.374   3,228.45   27,818,534.73

Describing Data

"Now what we have here is a failure to communicate."
—Strother Martin, *Cool Hand Luke* (1967)

After data has been edited for missing, extreme, and incorrect values, the next step in statistical analysis is to describe it accurately. Whether the goal is to describe supply and demand data, rental income data, cost data, demographic data, or sales data, appraisers must employ sound statistical methods to effectively describe the data and any trends.

The field of *statistics* is the branch of mathematics that covers the collection, description, and analysis of data. There are two distinct branches of statistics: descriptive statistics and inferential statistics. Both are equally important and distinctly different.

The branch that organizes and summarizes data into information that is meaningful is known as *descriptive statistics*. Descriptive statistics, as the name implies, is used to describe the data that has been collected. Since real estate appraisers often deal with relatively large populations of data (or sometimes a large sample of an even larger population), descriptive statistics gives them a manageable way to describe this data.

In contrast, *inferential statistics* is applied to arrive at reasonable conclusions about a larger population from the observed properties and relationships of the data that has been sampled. Inferential statistics is often used in tandem with probability, or chance, to draw a conclusion or make a prediction. Statistical inference is quite useful in providing explanations about the nature of unknown behaviors and processes. Before making any inferences, though, data must first be described effectively.

Descriptive statistics and graphic analysis are methods of presenting data and allowing it to speak for itself. These methods are used to describe the collected data before concluding what the collected data demonstrates or what relationships exist within the collected data. Descriptive statistics and graphic

probability
The possiblity that an event will occur, as expressed by the ratio of the number of actual occurrences to the total number of possible occurrences.

analysis provide a standard for an appraiser's observations. They present simple summaries in manageable form. They also provide a fundamental basis upon which quantitative and inferential analysis can build later in the valuation process.

This chapter covers the description of real estate data typically collected by real estate appraisers. The data from the industrial sales data set is revisited and described formally. Later chapters will employ inferential analysis techniques to perform actual valuation steps using the data described here. These steps can be used by appraisers in their own appraisal analyses. First, an appraiser must understand how to describe data using a single variable before moving on to two- and three-variable descriptive analysis and then to inferential analysis (see Figure 4.1).

Basic Descriptive Tools

In statistics, numbers by themselves convey relatively little information. The following values–$23,334, $45,312, $29,202, $31,202, and $32,361–mean little as listed on this page without context. By themselves they are raw numbers that have not been transformed into real information. It is critical to display the data in a meaningful context that provides useful information. As noted previously, the analytical process can be summarized as the transformation of market *data* into market *information*. The manner in which data is organized can further this process and lead to better understanding by both appraiser and client. Three general tools can be used to arrange and display data:

1. Tables
2. Graphs
3. Charts

Figure 4.1 **Navigation Chart**

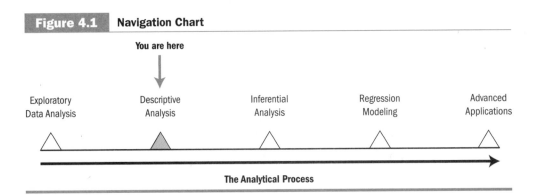

You are here

Exploratory Data Analysis

Descriptive Analysis

Inferential Analysis

Regression Modeling

Advanced Applications

The Analytical Process

Tables, or tabular displays, are useful devices for displaying raw data because they are orderly and are relatively easy to read. Tabular displays are useful for comparison, and they also can be used in making comparisons among differing data. One basic and important tabular display is the frequency table, which is constructed by dividing specific data values into intervals and counting the number of data points falling in each interval. Cumulative displays can also be presented in a frequency table. Frequency tables can be used for all data levels (i.e., nominal to ratio data).

Graphs can convey information from raw data better, but they must be effectively understood. Too much or too little data can render graphs less effective and hard to decipher. Certain chart forms lend themselves to certain data types, depending on the number of data intervals and data categories.

Charts combine both graphic and tabular data into single windows that convey information about a specific trend. Charts can be effective, too, but again analysts must understand how to use them properly. Fortunately, anyone who can construct tables and graphs should be able to build charts with ease.

The Descriptive Analysis Process

Figure 4.2 provides the basic road map for describing a single variable. The data set encountered in Chapter 3 can be described more effectively using the process shown in Figure 4.2 as a guide. For illustration purposes, an interval-level variable, **Improved Area**, and an ordinal variable, **Condition**, are used in the following descriptive analysis. SPSS is used as the analytical engine for the output. Graphic applications are also demonstrated along the way as additional descriptive tools.

Step 1: Arraying the Data
This step was already completed as part of the exploratory data analysis. Arraying is simply the sort function of a spreadsheet or other graphical software such as SPSS, based on one or more variables in the data set.

Step 2: Using Frequency Distributions
A frequency distribution arrays data automatically. For nominal or ordinal data, such as **Condition**, the frequency distribution can automatically array the data, assuming that the data is coded in order. Otherwise, the frequency distribution will sort the variable either alphabetically or numerically, depending on what the user tells the software. The

Figure 4.2   Single-Variable Descriptive Analysis

1. **Arraying the data**

   A listing of data in order of magnitude (ascending or descending)

   Useful for small data sets

2. **Frequency distribution**

   Shows the number of cases for
   - Each value of a variable in the case of binary and discrete data
   - Logical groups of values, termed *intervals* or *classes*, for interval and ratio data

   General rules for constructing a frequency distribution

   1. Choose at least 5 and not more than 15 intervals or classes
   2. Choose intervals or classes that
      - Do not overlap
      - Include all of the data
      - Are logical and easy to work with
   3. Count the number of cases in each interval

3. **Common measures of central tendency**

   Median
   - Half of observations above and below

   Mean
   - Computed by

         Summing all values

         Dividing by the number of cases
   - Can be highly influenced by extreme values

   Mode
   - Most frequently occurring value
   - Does not lend itself to statistical evaluations

4. **Common measures of dispersion**

   Range

   Quartiles

   Percentiles

   Standard deviation

   Steps in calculation:

   1. Find the mean
   2. Subtract the mean from each value
   3. Square the differences
   4. Sum the squared differences
   5. Divide by the number of cases less one (the result is termed the *variance*)
   6. Take the square root

   Interpretation depends on the data being normally distributed (approximating a bell-shaped curve)
   - 68% of data will lie within one standard deviation of the mean
   - 95% of data will lie within two standard deviations
   - 99% of data will lie within three standard deviations

5. **Coefficient of variation**

   Steps in calculation:

   1. Divide the standard deviation by the mean
   2. Multiply by 100

6. **One-variable charts and graphs**

   Histogram or bar chart
   - Values show horizontally
   - Counts or percentages shown vertically
   - Can be used for both discrete and continuous data

   Pie chart
   - Each slice of the pie represents the number or percentage of cases
   - The slices can be distinguished by different colors, patterns, or shades

Table 4.1	Building Condition				
		Frequency	Percent	Valid Percent†	Cumulative Percent
Valid	Average	326	72.6	72.6	72.6
	Excellent	22	4.9	4.9	77.5
	Fair	29	6.5	6.5	84.0
	Good	67	14.9	14.9	98.9
	Poor	5	1.1	1.1	100.0
	Total	449*	100.0	100.0	

* One sale was excluded from the 450-property data set because SPSS encountered a blank in one of the variable fields.

† "Valid Percent" refers to a data set with missing data. If five of the 449 sales were excluded because something was missing in each of those five cases, the *valid percent* would indicate relative percentages based on 444 sales. There are two types of missing data: 1) user-defined and 2) system-missing. The former occurs when the appraiser purposely codes a variable as missing, such as when a data element is unknown. The latter case occurs when a data element is literally missing in the data set. This can be due to a problem in data transmission or in the data set itself.

frequency distribution in Table 4.1 is based on the **Condition** variable in the industrial data set.

The frequency table ordered the variables in alphabetical order, not in the order that makes analytical sense:

1. Excellent
2. Good
3. Average
4. Fair
5. Poor

To do that, the variable would have to be recoded or numerically ordered, where 1 = Excellent, 2 = Good, 3 = Average, and so on. Table 4.2 recodes the variables in the proper order.

Table 4.2	Building Condition				
		Frequency	Percent	Valid Percent	Cumulative Percent
Valid	Excellent	22	4.9	4.9	4.0
	Good	67	14.9	14.9	19.8
	Average	326	72.6	72.6	92.4
	Fair	29	6.5	6.5	98.9
	Poor	5	1.1	1.1	100.0
	Total	449	100.0	100.0	

Once the data is arrayed correctly in the frequency table, the appraiser can examine the data easily. The table provides for an immediate indication of the distribution of the data across the categories as well as the most common and least common values. Graphically, the data can be displayed using a bar chart based on a frequency table, as shown in Figure 4.3.

Figure 4.3 | **Bar Chart**

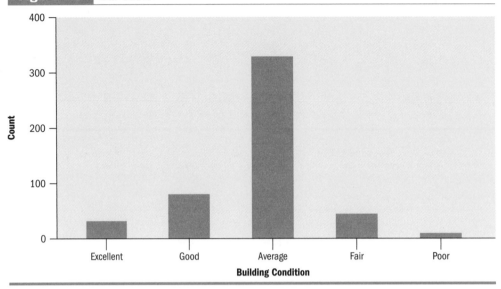

The bar chart provides an instantaneous picture of the data and a useful indication of the relative sizes of all categories. For example, it can easily be seen that the five sales of properties in poor condition may need further investigation; they may even be excluded from further analysis, particularly if the subject property is in average condition. The appraiser would need to determine whether an analysis of an industrial property in average condition benefits from the inclusion of industrial sales in above- or below-average condition. The important point here is that the appraiser can now make this determination from a whole-market perspective, using all of the market data as a reference. If the assignment involved a subject property *not* in average condition, the appraiser could decide that a sale property in a different condition would still merit inclusion based on further analysis of other comparable factors.

Using frequency tables for nominal data and ordinal data provides a good summary of the distribution of the data across each value. Table 4.3 is a frequency table of the nominal variable **House Style** for a data set of 150 house sales. Statistics such as the mean and standard deviation have no meaning at the nominal level and generally little meaning for ordinal data. For example, in the residential data set, what would the average of **House Style** be? Even so, important information can be derived from the frequency table. For example, note that the category

Table 4.3	Frequency Table
House Style	**Number of Sales**
Ranch	75
2-story	25
Bilevel	45
Split-level	5
Total	150

Split-level has only five sales. Such a small category indicates that this type of home may be relatively rare in this market. In addition, in the valuation analysis, the appraiser has only five sales of split-level homes to derive any adjustments for that house style.

For interval- and ratio-level data, frequency tables group data into manageable intervals. Listing all 449 industrial sales in the data set would result in a huge, multi-page table. Based on the array of data, the appraisers already knew that the smallest sale property totaled 1,200 square feet and the largest property totaled 454,682 square feet. To determine the size of the intervals, the next step is to examine the size of the subject property. If it is 250,000 square feet, the intervals used could be evenly spaced, such as at every 50,000 square feet. If the subject's improved area was closer to either extreme, the intervals chosen could be tightened around the subject. The two scenarios shown in Table 4.4 are based on a hypothetical subject property size of 23,000 square feet.

A few notes on the interval schemes: first, the intervals do not each have to have the same range. They do have to make appraisal sense, however. If the subject is 23,000 square feet in size, for example, then the appraiser is likely less interested in properties with improved areas over 50,000 square feet. Those upper sales may even be excluded from further consideration. In the first scenario, with the subject at 23,000 square feet, the intervals breaks are concentrated under 50,000 square feet, while the second scenario is more evenly spaced in 50,000-sq.-ft. intervals. Remember that the appraiser is free to recalibrate the intervals if they do not make sense.

Table 4.4	Size Intervals	
Intervals	**Scenario 1**	**Scenario 2**
1	0–5,000	0–50,000
2	5,001–10,000	50,001–100,000
3	10,001–15,000	100,001–150,000
4	15,001–20,000	150,001–200,000
5	20,001–25,000	200,001–250,000
6	25,001–30,000	250,001–300,000
7	30,001–35,000	300,001–350,000
8	35,000–40,000	350,001–400,000
9	40,001–45,000	400,001–450,000
10	Over 45,001	Over 450,001

Software manipulation makes any recalibration easy for even the largest data sets.

Table 4.5 illustrates a complete frequency table using the first scenario, with the subject set at 25,000 square feet. Sales over 45,000 square feet have been omitted from the data set. (Note that any reductions in the data, based on appraisal valuation norms, are completely acceptable at this stage.) At 25,000 square feet, the subject property lies within the range of 74.1% to 89.8% of the sales.

The next step would be to graphically illustrate the frequency distribution using a histogram (Figure 4.4). The histogram graphically depicts the distribution of the data, and the accompanying output provides some basic statistics (e.g., standard deviation, mean, number of data points).

Two sets of statistics help to define the data distribution, regardless of its distribution shape. One concerns measures of central tendency, a complex term for what most call the *average*. These statistics indicate the central points of data. The other set of statistics measures the variance of the distribution or the dispersion of data about the centerpoint. Both of these taken together can provide basic information about the data set. They allow for proper interpretation and, even more significantly, they allow for effectively associating one variable with another.

Step 3: Measures of Central Tendency

Once variables are arrayed (i.e., placed in order), the measures of central tendency—the mean, median, and mode—are easy to spot. These statistics are a straightforward way of indicating the clustering of the data around its center. Traditionally, appraisers

Table 4.5	Recorded Improved Area		
Valid	Frequency	Percent	Cumulative Percent
0–5,000	36	10.5	10.5
5,000–10,000	103	30.0	40.5
10,000–15,000	68	19.8	60.3
15,000–20,000	47	13.7	74.1
20,000–25,000	29	8.5	82.5
25,000–30,000	25	7.3	89.8
30,000–35,000	14	4.1	93.9
35,000–40,000	8	2.3	96.2
40,000–45,000	13	3.8	100.0
Total	343	100.0	

Figure 4.4 Histogram

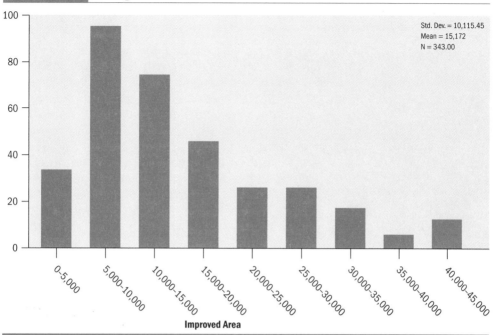

Std. Dev. = 10,115.45
Mean = 15,172
N = 343.00

Improved Area

Shapes of Data Distributions

In a *uniform distribution*, data is more or less equally distributed across all values. *Skewed data* clusters at one end of the range of data. *Normally distributed data* can be illustrated with the familiar bell-shaped curve.

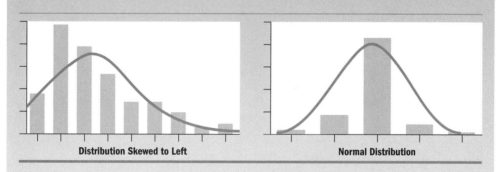

Distribution Skewed to Left   **Normal Distribution**

Although a normally distributed distribution is often found in behavioral data, it is not always desired. For example, when analyzing sales across a defined sales period, the data should be more or less equally distributed across the time period. Please note that data distributions described as normally distributed, uniformly distributed, or skewed refer to *interval-* and *ratio*-level data only. Real estate data is typically skewed and not normal.

have been told not to use any of these measures of central tendency in their valuation conclusions. The authors believe that this comes from the misapplication of the mean average, where appraisers have previously used the average sale price of a group of comparable properties to value the subject property without appropriate adjustments.

While this is certainly not standard practice anymore, the use of the average when dealing with adjusted units of comparison is acceptable under certain circumstances. For example, if an adjustment grid with five comparable sales results in a narrow band of unit values, and no sales among the five are clearly the best comparables, then the use of the mean or median average is completely reasonable and supportable. Again, the appraiser must be prepared in this instance to defend the adjustment employed and the conclusion that there is no further weighting required among the comparable sales. There is no need to summarily dismiss the use of the average unit value based on some outdated prejudice. In this example, a more relevant criticism could be the use of *only* five sales.

The three most common measures of central tendency are types of averages, although the mean is most commonly referred to as the *average*. These statistics are calculated as follows:

Mean	Median	Mode
sum of values / no. of values	midpoint value	most common value or range of values

The Mean. The mean is the most powerful statistical measure of central tendency, given its use in determining other statistics (such as the standard deviation) and in regression analysis. It weights all of the data points equally and does not attempt to modify the distribution. It is also the most prone to extreme values, whether large or small.

The mean is derived by summing a group of numbers and then dividing the sum by the number of values. For instance, given the set of values 1, 2, 3, 4, 5, 6, 7, 8, and 9, the mean is calculated as follows:

$$(1 + 2 + 3 + 4 + 5 + 6 + 7 + 8 + 9) / 9 = 45 / 9 = 5$$

In comparison to the median, the mean not only takes into account the location of each point, but it also considers the distance between each point, making the mean the most powerful measure of central tendency with respect to the levels of measurement.

Some appraisal experts decry the use of measures of central tendency and yet promote the use of paired sales analysis, a crude adjustment method. Using a single property that has been resold to apply market adjustments is perhaps the method that least represents market behavior (i.e., the actions of the entire range of participants).

The Median. The median value represents the mid-point in the array, which means that half of the data points are less than the median and the other half are greater. Because it is a fixed data point within the set (or the average of the two middle data points for a data set with an even number of elements), it is less influenced by extreme values. If an entry for 100 is added to the data set used to calculate the mean in the preceding section, the mean value would be more affected than the median. (This also depends on the number of sales, of course.) The range of data is still an important consideration, and the distance between the median and the upper and lower bounds of the data set reveals much about the shape of the distribution curve. Also, the median can be used with ordinal level data, as well as interval- and ratio-level data.

The Mode. The mode is defined as the most frequently occurring value in a distribution, and it can be used with data measured at all levels. When a distribution contains more than one category with the same number of observations and that is the highest number of occurrences, the distribution is called *bimodal.* If there are numerous scores that occur the same number of times and that would each qualify as the mode (i.e., being the most frequently occurring value), the distribution is termed *multimodal.* It is important to note that as the number of modes increases, the mode becomes less helpful as a descriptor of the data. A critical weakness of the mode is that a data set can often have no mode–i.e., each observation may be entirely unique, and therefore the only useful information that the mode will be able to provide about the data is that it is uniformly distributed.

Of the measures of central tendency, the mode is used least often, but it can still provide a statistical measure that appraisers can find useful. Although the mode is technically the value with the most occurrences, it can also be applied to a group of values. For example, if the sales array for the industrial data set has most sales occurring between $125,000 and $130,000, the modality of that data can be expressed by that range. The selection of the most comparable sale properties can also be expressed as a modality, if appropriate. Though the mode can be used for all of the levels of data (nominal, ordinal, and interval/ratio), it is the only measure of central tendency that can be used for the nominal scale.

Figure 4.5 illustrates the mean, median, and mode of the variable **Sale Price**. In a line graph like Figure 4.5, the mode is the peak of the distribution, where the

> Sales data is typically skewed to the right, made up of the sales of higher-priced properties. This is why the median sale price is used in the analysis of housing price inflation.

sale price amount with the highest number of sales is located. The median is seen next at the fiftieth percentile (i.e., with 50% of the sales below and 50% of the sales above). The mean is next; it is most influenced by the higher sale prices to the right. Without looking at the graphical representation in Figure 4.5, the appraiser could determine that the sales were skewed to the right by the distance and location of the mean from the other measures of central tendency.

Step 4: Determining Variation

The measures of central tendency tell observers about the data within a distribution. What it does not explicitly disclose is the nature of the data variance on either side of the mean, median, and mode–i.e., what is known as the *variance*. Before any proper evaluation can be concluded for a descriptive analysis of a single variable, or prior to any comparison to another variable, the variance must be measured and interpreted.

For example, a data set with an array of sale prices that have a mean of $100,000, with a range between $75,000 and $140,000, may have much less variance than another data set with the same mean but a minimum value of $25,000 and a maximum value of $500,000. In this example, to simply say that the two arrayed sales data sets are similar because they have the same mean value is misleading. The similarity of the means reveals nothing about the different variances of each distribution. (Figure 4.6 illustrates two data sets with the same mean, median,

Figure 4.5 Line Graph

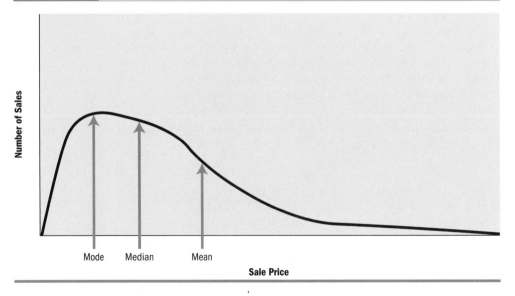

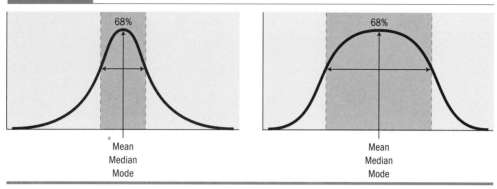

and mode but with very different variances.) To illustrate those differences statistically, standard measures of variation are needed.

There are four basic measures of variance that appraisers should understand:

- Range
- Standard deviation
- Coefficient of variation
- Coefficient of dispersion

All of these measures of variation focus on interval- or ratio-level data.

Range. The simplest measure of variance is the *range*, which is defined as the difference between the highest and lowest scores in a distribution. The range of a distribution can be calculated by subtracting the smallest value from the largest value to give a single numeric value, but it is also common to state the range as the two extreme values.

The following example is of a small office sales data set, using the variable **Improved Area**:

Sale	Improved Area (in Square Feet)
1	6,500
2	8,064
3	10,000
4	10,080
5	12,400
6	14,000
7	17,787
8	18,540
9	20,772
10	25,466
Maximum value	25,466
Minimum value	− 6,500
Range	18,966

While the range is straightforward in its calculation and easy to understand, there are some disadvantages. The range takes into account only two values in the distribution–the highest and lowest points. The remaining values in the distribution are ignored. An additional consideration is that the larger the number of points, the greater the likelihood that extreme outliers will be included, thus increasing the size of the range in a manner that would make the range of data appear to be significantly greater than it is. Is the data overall very stable and comparable to the subject, or is it distributed across too wide a range of values, requiring editing? Knowing the range is a good start, but it is not enough. Note that since the data has already been arrayed by the **Improved Area** variable, the range is easy to calculate.

To understand the data more clearly, knowledge of the way in which the values are spread out within this range is obviously required. To evaluate the dispersion of a variable, an analyst might wonder if the values are almost all clustered around the middle or if there are some very low and very high values. Sometimes a distribution can be broken down into four equal parts, each called a *quartile*. A *quartile* is defined as a subset of the distribution that holds one-fourth of the data points. The quartiles are commonly labeled Q_1, Q_2, Q_3, and Q_4. The upper-quartile (Q_1) contains the top one-fourth of the data points. The *inter-quartile range* is that range that contains the middle 50% of the data points (Q_2 and Q_3). This range is not influenced by extreme values in the data set, as is the overall range. Sometimes a distribution can be divided even further into *deciles*, i.e., subgroupings containing one-tenth of the data points.

For all they reveal about a data set, the range, quartiles, and various measures of the middle do not fully depict the distribution of the values. The next step in describing a distribution is developing some sort of variation measure of one variable that can be compared to other variables, allowing an appraiser to demonstrate that the variance of a particular variable is greater or less than another.

The Standard Deviation and Coefficient of Variation. Since the mean value is the arithmetic middle of an array of data points, the variance is measured by the numeric difference between each value and the mean, as shown in Table 4.6. The 10 properties have an average (mean) size of 14,361 square feet. The individual variances are represented by column D, which is the difference between each property's actu-

A	B	C	D
Sale	**Improved Area**	**Mean**	**Difference**
1	6,500	14,361	-7,861
2	8,064	14,361	-6,297
3	10,000	14,361	-4,361
4	10,080	14,361	-4,281
5	12,400	14,361	-1,961
6	14,000	14,361	-361
7	17,787	14,361	3,426
8	18,540	14,361	4,179
9	20,772	14,361	6,411
10	25,466	14,361	11,105
Total Difference			0

Table 4.6   **Difference from Mean Size**

al size and the mean size of the group. Roughly half of the properties are smaller than the mean and half are larger, so the resulting variances are negative for the smaller properties and positive for the larger properties. More importantly, the sum of the variances is zero. This is true for all data sets, no matter what the range or shape of the distribution.

Statisticians have developed several methods to deal with the problem inherent in calculating the total variance. The most common is to square the values in Column D. Since the square of a negative number is positive, all of the values for variance become positive, and adding them together creates no problem. The sum of the squared values is then divided by the number of sales (less one if the data set represents a sample of all properties). The average of the summed differences is known in statistics as the *variance of the distribution.* Note that the variance can be a very large number because it is the sum of the squared differences.

The *standard deviation* is the square root of the variance. Because the squaring process is reversed in the calculation of the standard deviation, it serves as a measure of spread whose value is based on the same scale as the values or observations in the distribution itself. Table 4.7 illustrates the calculations of both the variance and standard deviation for the 10-property data set. Column E is the squared value of Column D. The variance is simply the sum of Column E divided by ten sales less one because this is a sample and not the entire population (i.e., nine

Table 4.7	Variance and Standard Deviation			
A	**B**	**C**	**D**	**E**
Sale	**Improved Area**	**Mean**	**Difference**	**Squared Difference**
1	6,500	14,361	-7,861	61,795,321
2	8,064	14,361	-6,297	39,652,209
3	10,000	14,361	-4,361	19,018,321
4	10,080	14,361	-4,281	18,326,961
5	12,400	14,361	-1,961	3,845,521
6	14,000	14,361	-361	130,321
7	17,787	14,361	3,426	11,737,476
8	18,540	14,361	4,179	17,464,041
9	20,772	14,361	6,411	41,100,921
10	25,466	14,361	11,105	123,321,025
				336,392,117
			Number of sales	9
			Variance	37,376,902
			Standard deviation	6,114

Whenever you are calculating *sample* statistics, statistical theory requires a little modification to the formula for standard deviation. This is because the sample represents a subset of the entire population. For example, if you have a sample of only three sales and calculate the average, you have reduced the explanatory power of the sample by one observation. In other words, the mean reduces the number of "pure" observations by one. Termed *degrees of freedom*, this fact requires us to reduce the number of sales by one. This is true whether the sample has three observations or three thousand observations. Note, of course, that as the sample size grows larger and approaches the population size, the effects of this reduction diminishes.

sales). The standard deviation is the square root of this total. Note that the values in Column E are much greater at the tails–that is, the endpoints of the range (Sales 1, 2, 9, and 10).

The standard deviation can be used to predict the total percentage of values within its boundaries about the mean. For example, the mean average size of these properties is 14,361 square feet, and the standard deviation is 6,114 square feet. With an adequate number of sales (usually over 30), an analyst could make some predictions about the number of sales within one, two, or three standard deviations about the mean, *assuming that the distribution is normal.* In this case, it would be reasonable to conclude that approximately 68% of the properties have improved areas within one standard deviation below and above the mean value, or between 8,247 square feet and 20,475 square feet, as shown by the shaded area in Table 4.8. Six of the ten properties are within one standard deviation of the mean of 14,361 square feet. Whether this is good or bad from an appraisal standpoint depends on the appraiser's judgment concerning the effects of improvement size on office properties.

The limitation of the standard deviation is that it is expressed as a unit of the variable it is measuring. The appraiser can compare the standard deviation of one variable with the standard deviation of the *same* variable from another data set. For example, if the appraiser was involved in a court case against another appraiser, one side's data set could be compared to the

Table 4.8	Properties Within One Standard Deviation of the Mean			
Sale	Improved Area	Mean	Difference	Squared Difference
1	6,500	14,361	-7,861	61,795,321
2	8,064	14,361	-6,297	39,652,209
3	10,000	14,361	-4,361	19,018,321
4	10,080	14,361	-4,281	18,326,961
5	12,400	14,361	-1,961	3,845,521
6	14,000	14,361	-361	130,321
7	17,787	14,361	3,426	11,737,476
8	18,540	14,361	4,179	17,464,041
9	20,772	14,361	6,411	41,100,921
10	25,466	14,361	11,105	123,321,025
				336,392,117
			Number of sales	9
			Variance	37,376,902
			Standard deviation	6,114

data set used by the opposing party, and if one data set consistently had lower standard deviations across all variables used, then that data set could be demonstrated to be superior to the other side's data set. What cannot be compared is the standard deviation between two different variables. In addition, if the appraiser has only a single variable under scrutiny, there needs to be a method to determine that the standard deviation is small enough to be statistically significant.

One of the most powerful statistics that appraisers can employ is the *coefficient of variation* (the COV). This measure of average variation about the mean value is easy to calculate and easy to interpret for appraisers and non-appraisers alike. The COV is calculated by dividing the standard deviation by the mean. In the office sales data set, the COV would be calculated as follows:

$$\frac{\text{standard deviation}}{\text{mean}} \quad \frac{6,114}{14,361} = 0.426 = \text{COV}$$

Convention transforms the quotient of 0.426 into a percentage value of 42.6%. This percentage can now be compared with other variables directly. If the variable for total land area has a COV of 30%, then the appraiser can conclude that this distribution is more concentrated than the improved area distribution, which had a COV of 42.6%. The ability to compare the average deviation across variables has important applications in later chapters.

Coefficient of Dispersion. The *coefficient of dispersion* (COD) is similar to the COV but is useful for smaller data sets (less than 30 properties). The COD uses the absolute average deviation instead of the standard deviation to determine the average deviation in a distribution. It also uses the median average, as opposed to the mean average. Because smaller data sets can have non-normal distributions, making the mean and standard deviation unreliable, the COD provides a more robust measurement of dispersion in those situations.

> Even with a data set as small as 10, the COD can be an effective measure of accuracy, as long as the data is fairly uniform.

The average absolute deviation solves the problem of negative and positive variance about the average by using the absolute value of each individual difference. No squaring of the differences is necessary. The resulting column of positive differences is then added together. The sum is next divided by the number of properties to arrive at the COD. Table 4.9 uses the same 10 office sales from earlier examples and computes the COD in a similar manner to the COV. The results in this example are also similar— 42.6% for the COV and 37.5% for the COD.

The COD is preferred over the COV for small data sets and for distributions that are not normally distributed. Both measure the average deviation and can be compared across different variables as a measurement of the dispersion of data values about the mean. As the number of data points in a variable grows and

Table 4.9	Coefficient of Dispersion			
A	**B**	**C**	**D**	**E**
Sale	**Improved Area**	**Mean**	**Difference**	**Absolute Difference**
1	6,500	13,200	-6,700	6,700
2	8,064	13,200	-5,136	5,136
3	10,000	13,200	-3,200	3,200
4	10,080	13,200	-3,120	3,120
5	12,400	13,200	-800	800
6	14,000	13,200	800	800
7	17,787	13,200	4,587	4,587
8	18,540	13,200	5,340	5,340
9	20,772	13,200	7,572	7,572
10	25,466	13,200	12,266	12,266
				49,521
			Number of sales	10*
			Average absolute deviation	4,952
			COD	37.5%

* Note that the number of sales for COV calculations is one less than for COD calculations using the same data set because the calculation of COD does not require the loss of a degree of freedom as the calcuation of COV does.

the distribution approaches a normal shape, the mean and median move closer to one another. The same can be said for the COD and COV.

Describing Two Variables

Figure 4.7 outlines the process for describing and comparing the interaction of two independent variables or the interaction between the dependent variable and a single independent variable. These analyses allow appraisers to develop defensible, quantifiable adjustments for all three approaches to value.

Levels of Data. Although the level of data for each variable can limit the application of specific statistical tests, it does not prohibit the examination of two variables of differing levels. A nominal-level variable such as **Neighborhood** can be easily compared to a continuous ratio-level variable such as **Sale Price**. In fact, many tools used to describe interaction between two variables favor nominal and ordinal scale data because there are generally fewer value categories.

Crosstab Tables. A frequency table with two variables is termed a *crosstab table* (or *contingency table* in older statistical texts). The setup of a crosstab table is similar to a spreadsheet, with one variable arrayed by row and the other arrayed by column. Like a frequency table, ratio- and interval-level data may need to be summarized into intervals so the table does not become too large. Table 4.10 examines the 343 sales

---

Figure 4.7	**Descriptive Analysis for Two or More Variables**

1. Crosstabulations
2. Scatter diagrams
   - The dependent variable is shown on the vertical axis.
   - The independent variable is shown on the horizontal axis.
3. Breakdowns
4. Line graph (polygon graph)
   - Vertical axis: Typically contains measures of central tendency for the dependent variable.
   - Horizontal axis: Typically the independent variable is shown on the horizontal axis.

Multiple variables
   - May include several variables
   - Same variable can be shown for different strata

Three-way comparisons
   - Contingency tables
   - 3-D diagrams
       Scatter diagram of a dependent variable versus independent variables
       Requires 3-D graphics

---

of properties under 50,000 square feet in the industrial data set, comparing the variables **Age** with **Bldgcond** (i.e., building condition).

The **Age** variable was recoded into 10-year intervals for ease of use in the crosstab table. Some interesting comparisons can be made. First, note that **Age** and **Bldgcond** seem to be related, at least at the extreme categories. For example, all of the buildings in excellent condition were less than 10 years old. Four of the five buildings in poor condition were at least 31 years old. If the variables are related, then an analyst would probably want to exclude one of these variables in any further modeling; otherwise, the interaction between these variables could cause problems.

In terms of basic comparability, the appraiser now has a framework to determine if certain whole classes of properties, as defined by the variables examined in the table, should be excluded from further analysis. If the goal is to value a single property, it may become less critical to include properties from other categories that are not truly comparable.

Multi-Variable Graphs. Two types of graphs lend themselves to two-variable analysis. Line graphs (or, to use the technical term, *polygon graphs*) and scatter plot graphs can easily illustrate the interaction between two variables. Figure 4.8 shows a scatter plot graph, using the same industrial sales data set and plotting the sale price per square foot and gross building area.

The graph illustrates the same relationship between the **Sale Price per Square Foot** and **Improved Area**. Although there is a significant amount of variation caused by other variables not considered, an overall downward trend is indicated.

Table 4.10	Age and Building Condition Crosstabulation					
	Bldgcond					
Age	**Excellent**	**Good**	**Average**	**Fair**	**Poor**	**Total**
0-10	17	23	17	0	0	57
11-20	0	8	67	2	0	77
21-30	0	11	64	7	1	83
31-40	0	3	66	4	2	75
41-50	0	0	26	6	0	32
51-60	0	0	5	3	0	8
61-70	0	0	1	1	0	2
71-80	0	0	3	1	1	5
80+	0	0	3	0	1	4
Total	17	45	252	24	5	343

Using SPSS, further refinements in these graphs could include color coding using a third variable (such as **Building Age**) as well as labeling.

Economic attributes can also be described graphically. The line (i.e., polygon) graph in Figure 4.9 illustrates the relationship of the median reported direct capitalization rate at the time of sale to the age of the property. The graph clearly indicates that as the age of an industrial property increases the direct capitalization rate also increases. A scatter plot graph could describe the same association but in a more convoluted manner. Line graphs also allow for the comparison of three or more variables. In most cases, line graphs compare two variables using summary data (i.e., averages) for one or both variables. Otherwise, with 343 data points, the line graph would try to connect every point.

Assessor models typically value whole classes of properties and therefore must include a much broader scope of properties. This is one of the major differences in mass appraisal applications between assessment appraisers and single-property (i.e., fee) appraisers.

Comparing Three or More Variables

The descriptive analysis of three or more variables can be competently performed in SPSS, but caution needs to be exercised in terms of complexity level. A

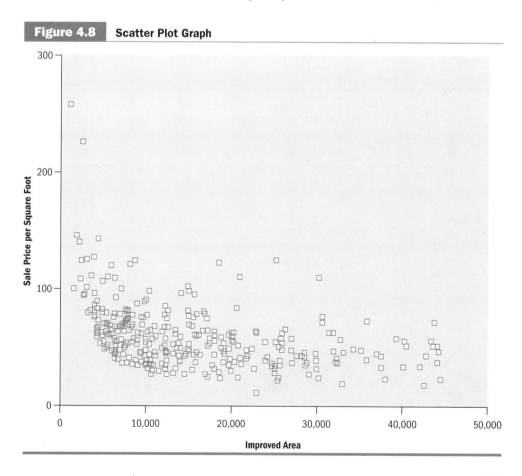

Figure 4.8   **Scatter Plot Graph**

Figure 4.9   Line (Polygon) Graph

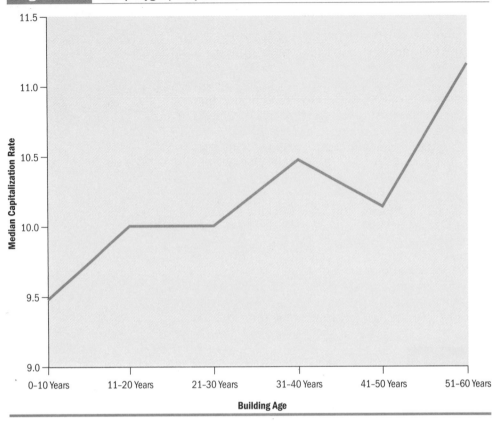

three-way comparison of variables needs to be guided by the appraisal questions at hand. For example, a three-way analysis involving scale variables, such as gross building area, number of parking spaces, and total land area, can be presented with little conceptual difficulty. Often if the third variable is the sale price or a location variable, a three-way analysis can be accomplished without undue complexity. Realize, however, that such multi-variate analyses are usually best performed as part of an appraisal valuation modeling process using multi-linear regression (MLR) or another statistical modeling process.

A Note about Software

Most of the single-variable descriptive analysis can be performed with either a spreadsheet or statistical software package. Some of the arithmetic calculations and table arrays can also be performed manually, although it can become too cumbersome with data sets larger than 20 or 30 properties.

Spreadsheets can perform two-variable descriptive analysis fairly competently, including the associated graphical presentations. Anything more complex would require a software package such as SPSS or MiniTab.

CHAPTER 5

Special Applications

"Jumping out of a perfectly functional aircraft at 10,000 feet is not a natural act."

– Clint Eastwood, *Heartbreak Ridge* (1983)

Armed with the proper analytical tools to effectively describe the market data needed to value the subject property, you should now be ready to make that jump, despite any reservations about the altitude. No longer should appraisers look at the mountain of data on their desk and yearn for the old days, when three sales were enough (along with four rental comps). But appraisers are still not completely comfortable with how all the data fits together in the valuation process. After describing the market data, then what? A complete valuation model still feels too sophisticated, too difficult. The goal of this chapter is to move toward the complete valuation model for the subject property by applying earlier lessons to specific valuation questions that can be answered using simple one- and two-variable models and analyses.

As noted previously, there are two main branches of statistical analysis, descriptive analysis and inferential analysis. The previous chapter discussed in detail some important descriptive tools appraisers can use to describe data sets. This chapter and the remaining chapters of this book focus on inferential statistics–the tools analysts use to infer relationships between variables. For appraisal, this typically involves the sale price (i.e., the dependent variable) and a set of property attributes (the independent variables).

As the navigation chart indicates (Figure 5.1), the applications of inferential analysis discussed in this chapter should be performed after exploratory data analysis and descriptive analysis have been completed. The following case studies of inferential applications use several commercial and residential data sets.

Figure 5.1 — Navigation Chart

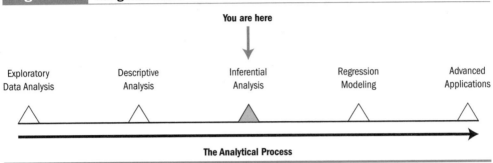

You are here

Exploratory Data Analysis · Descriptive Analysis · Inferential Analysis · Regression Modeling · Advanced Applications

The Analytical Process

Case Study 1: Comparing Two Groups (Application of the t-Test)

When comparing two individual properties, appraisers do not have to use statistical analysis. For example, if House 1 has a gross living area of 2,450 square feet and House 2 has a gross living area of 2,700 square feet, then an appraiser would simply make comparisons using basic arithmetic. For example:

- House 2 is larger than House 1 (2,700 square feet > 2,450 square feet).
- House 2 has 250 square feet more gross living area than House 1 does (2,700 – 2,450 = 250).
- House 2 has approximately 10% more gross living area than House 1 does (2,700 ÷ 2,450 = 1.1020, rounded and restated as +10%).

As a further example, assume that a buyer was looking for a home with a minimum size of 2,500 square feet. This example is another simple comparison of two properties: the proposed acquisition property (Candidate property 2), with a size of 2,700 square feet, and the ideal property that exists in the mind of the prospective buyer.

The following statements are reasonable conclusions:

- Candidate property 2 exceeds the minimum criteria for building size (2,700 square feet > 2,500 square feet).
- Candidate property 2 has 200 more square feet of gross living area than the minimum criteria established for gross living area (2,700 – 2,500 = 200).
- Candidate property 2 has a gross living area that is 8% greater than the established minimum gross living area (2,700 ÷ 2,500 = 1.08, restated as +8%).

When comparing a single property to a group of properties, however, these statements and comparisons will not suffice. For example, suppose a buyer is looking at a multitenant income-producing office/warehouse property with 45% of its area currently finished as office space. The buyer, realizing that the level of office finish is greater than the norm, might want some help evaluating the risk of the sustainability of the income attributable to the current level of office finish. An analyst could survey the competitive industrial buildings in the market neighborhood for the amount of finished office space and examine the distribution of that data to answer this risk/probability question. The results of such a survey are summarized in Figure 5.2.

From the information on this market area, an appraiser can observe that an office finish of 45% is greater than typical. The median is within the 21%-30% interval. Of the 68 buildings surveyed, 12 had office finishes comparable to (41%–50%) or greater than the subject building. Thus, it would be reasonable to conclude that the probability of sustaining or exceeding the higher income attributable to the atypical office finish (45%) is about 12-in-68, or about 18% (12 ÷ 68 = 0.17647, rounded and restated as 18%).

Comparing two groupings is a much more interesting situation and is quite different from the comparisons of two individual properties or of an individual property to a group. Suppose an appraiser wants to determine the impact of proximity to a golf

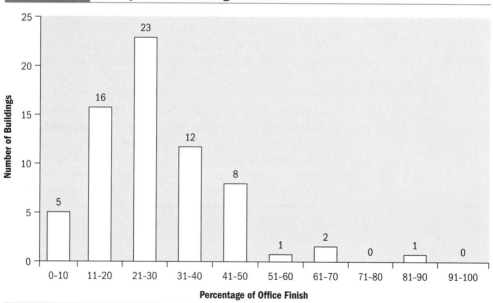

Figure 5.2   **Distribution of Percentage of Office Finish in Subject Industrial Neighborhood**

course on single-family housing in a particular market. This would be a simple problem if there were no variation in each of the two groupings of homes. If *all* properties in the neighborhood had exactly the same physical attributes, with the only difference being location on or off the golf course, then the analyst could easily compare properties that sold with or without this attribute. Such examples seldom occur in the real world, of course. So just how are two groupings with varying attributes compared?

One easy method would be to compare the maximum sale price from each group and note the difference. Would that comparison accomplish the goal of revealing information about the entire neighborhood? The answer is no, since in reality both groups are composed of many individual data points. A meaningful comparison would have to account for all data points, not just one data point (e.g., the greatest) in the grouping. The mean or median of each of the two groups is commonly used as a central measure for the entire collection of data points in each grouping. But these measures alone do not give the entire answer. The distribution of the group is also critical and, once again, it is the variation in the distribution that plays a key role.

The statistical *t-test* compares the means of two groupings and assesses whether they are *statistically* different from each other at a predefined level of significance. The equation for the t-test considers two components:

1. The difference in means
2. The variation of the two distributions[1]

The formula for the t-test is a ratio. The numerator of the ratio is just the difference between the two means. The denominator is a measure of the dispersion of the data. This formula is essentially another example of the signal-to-noise metaphor in statistical analysis. The difference between the means is the *signal* that, for example, tells an analyst that these two neighborhoods are experiencing different pricing in the marketplace while the denominator of the formula measures the variability that is essentially the statistical *noise* that makes it harder to see the real differences between the groups.

In the following example, a large mountain resort neighborhood in Colorado was chosen for comparison, with home sales occurring both on the golf course and away from the golf course. The his-

---

1. To be precise, the t-test uses the standard deviation, which is the square root of the variance.

togram in Figure 5.3 was derived from this data set, examining *all* sales. The 113 total sales have an average sale price of $123.70 per square foot, with a range of $100.50 to $144.77 per square foot. The distribution in Figure 5.3 is approximately normal; the additional question is whether the two groups (on a golf course and off a golf course) are statistically different. The histograms in Figure 5.4 separate the two groups.

Figure 5.3   **Sales of All Properties**

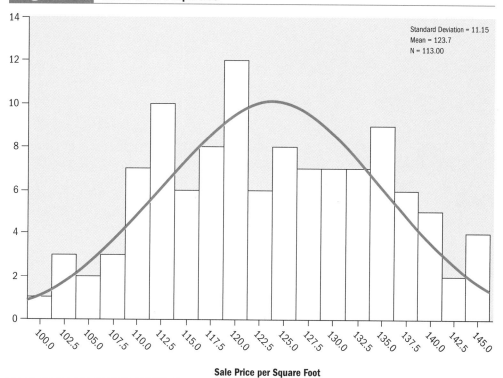

Standard Deviation = 11.15
Mean = 123.7
N = 113.00

Sale Price per Square Foot

Figure 5.4   **House Sales On and Off a Golf Course**

GOLF: .00 (off golf course)

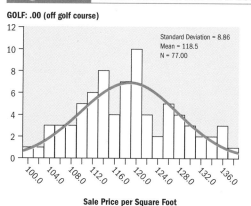

Standard Deviation = 8.86
Mean = 118.5
N = 77.00

Sale Price per Square Foot

GOLF: 1.00 (on golf course)

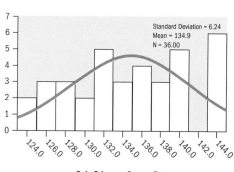

Standard Deviation = 6.24
Mean = 134.9
N = 36.00

Sale Price per Square Foot

The 77 sale properties that are not located adjacent to a golf course are clearly normally distributed. The other group, with 36 sales, is not as normally distributed. SPSS easily tests for significant differences between two groups, under the *independent sample t-tests* procedure. This particular t-test compares the means and distributions of the two groups. The appraiser needs to ensure that any measured difference is due to the factor under consideration–in this case, location on or off a golf course.

SPSS produced the output in Table 5.1 from the sales data set illustrated in Figures 5.3 and 5.4. The first row of the t-test output assumes that the variances about each mean value are similar. The second row can be used when the variances are not similar, as in this example. The significance column, which is shaded, indicates the probability that any differences in the mean values of each group are due to random chance, meaning in this case that there would be no statistical difference. This measure is a function of both the actual distance between each mean and the variation of each group. A greater difference between the means and a narrower distribution of each group both decrease the chance that the observed difference is false. Figure 5.5 illustrates this concept.

In the graph on the left in Figure 5.5, both the mean and the distribution about the means for both groups are clearly separate. In the graph on the right, the distinction is much more blurred. In that graph, a

Table 5.1	SPSS Output

Group Statistics

GOLF		N	Mean	Std. Deviation	Std. Error Mean
SPSF	.00	77	118.5085	8.85753	1.00941
	1.00	36	134.9102	6.24347	1.04058

Independent Samples Test

		Levene's Test for Equality of Variances		t-test for Equality of Means					95% Confidence Interval of the Difference	
		F	Sig.	t	df	Sig. (2-tailed)	Mean Difference	Std. Error Difference	Lower	Upper
SPSF	Equal variances assumed	4.159	.044	-9.999	111	.000	-16.4016	1.64038	-19.65215	-13.15112
	Equal variances not assumed			-11.314	93.666	.000	-16.4016	1.44973	-19.28024	-13.52303

Figure 5.5 Distribution Graphs

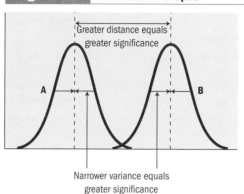

Greater distance equals greater significance

A   B

Narrower variance equals greater significance

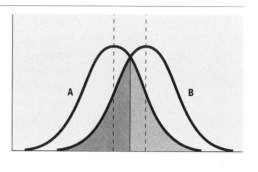

A   B

Box and Whisker Plots

A strong graphic used to demonstrate the differences between two groups is the box and whisker plot. This data display also indicates the relative spread and central points between multiple groups. The box and whisker plot is of the same home sale data used elsewhere in the chapter.

The shaded box in both plots represents the data between 25% and 75%; the shaded line in the center of the box marks the 50% percentile (i.e., the median value). The whiskers (t-shaped line segments) below the boxes represent the lower 25% of the data, while the upper whiskers represent the upper 25% of the data. The figure below compares a histogram for the whole data set with the corresponding box and whisker plot.

The box and whisker plot provides for an easy display of the data's distribution and measure of central tendency. While it is a powerful graphic tool, readers *must* be educated about its use and interpretation *before* it is presented in any appraisal. Many find this graphic hard to interpret without prior exposure to the format; unlike other graphs it is not intuitively obvious at first glance. Once understood, box and whisker plots can be used to compare distributions and the data variance about the median for several categories. Extreme outlier values can also be identified using this type of graph.

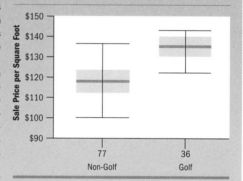

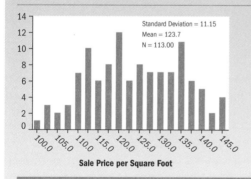

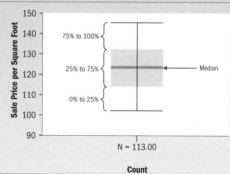

large portion of Group A, highlighted by the orange shared area, overlaps with the distribution of Group B. Likewise, a significant portion of Group B, highlighted by the grey shaded area, overlaps with Group A. The tests for significance measure this overlap area; the smaller the statistic, the better. In the two graphs in Figure 5.5, the significance of the graph on the left would be near zero, meaning that the observed difference is likely a true difference and not created by random chance. The graph on the right, however, would carry with it a 50% chance that the difference between Group A and B is false; that is, there is no difference. An appraiser testifying in court that there is a difference between both groups of sales would likely prefer the graph on the left.

Another measure used to test for significance is the confidence interval. Confidence intervals are provided in the SPSS t-test output shown in Table 5.2. In that output, the mean difference column shows the difference between the mean sale price per square foot of each group. In this example, the mean sale price of home sales near a golf course is $134.91 per square foot, while the mean of sales of homes not on a golf course is $118.51 per square foot, resulting in a mean difference of $16.40 per square foot. The standard error statistic is the variance of this mean difference. If the means were closer and the variance of each group was wider (as in the graph on the right side of Figure 5.5), then the standard error would be much larger. The confidence interval is based on a multiple of the standard error. The 95% confidence interval, for example, is based on the standard error times two on either side of the mean difference, as follows:

95% Confidence Interval Construction		
Low	**Mean**	**High**
Standard Error × 2		Standard Error × 2
Mean − (1.45 × 2)		Mean + (1.45 × 2)
$13.50	$16.40	$19.30

The confidence interval indicates that there is a real difference between the groups. If either the low or the high intervals included the value zero, then the difference could be due to random chance.

Other t-test applications can be used in appraisal. The *paired samples t-test* is similar to the independent sample t-test except that rather than having two separate groups, the paired samples t-test compares the same variable twice. This could be used if the appraiser has paired sales for many properties. The

Table 5.2	SPSS Output									
	Levene's Test for Equality of Variances		t-test for Equality of Means							
									95% Confidence Interval of the Difference	
	F	Sig.	t	df	Sig. (2-tailed)	Mean Difference	Std. Error Difference		Lower	Upper
SPSF Equal variances assumed	4.159	.044	-9.999	111	.000	-16.4016	1.64038		-19.65215	-13.15112
Equal variances not assumed			-11.314	93.666	.000	-16.4016	1.44973		-19.28024	-13.52303

difference in data that a t-test measures can be related to a single factor, such as the proximity of a golf course, or to a change over time, as in a paired sale analysis. Also, the factor being tested could be positive or negative.

The appraiser needs to recognize limitations with this type of analysis. The t-test provides a quick, but potentially misleading, test for significant differences. If the properties in one group differ significantly from the other group based on factors not being tested, then the t-test could ascribe the difference to the wrong variable. For example, if the factor under scrutiny was lake frontage but the homes surrounding the lake were smaller, ranch-style homes while the predominant style of homes not along the lake were larger, two-story homes, then any significant difference could be due to difference in style and scale, not solely to the lake frontage. The appraiser would have to test all three (and possibly more) variables in a comprehensive valuation model. (This type of analysis will be presented later in this book.)

One way to decrease the possible *confounding* effects of other variables is to use larger data sets. This can reduce the differences in the effect of other factors. Of course, the appraiser may have limited sales in one of the groups, rendering statistical testing moot. Whatever the conditions, the results must make appraisal sense and common sense. A statistically significant t-test that indicates that homes abutting golf courses sell for *less* than homes away from golf courses needs further scrutiny.

All of the examples in Case Study 1 were tested using SPSS. The t-test can be manipulated manually and with a spreadsheet, but the calculations for larger data sets are cumbersome. For a manual calculation, the appraiser would have to use a book of statistical tables to test whether the t-test ratios were significant.

Case Study 2: Paired Sales Analysis

As noted previously, the authors are not fans of paired sales analysis, especially when data is available that supports a more accurate and logically supportable valuation model. Sometimes, however, paired data may be the best available market data–although this is more an indication of the limitations of the market data than a desired method of analysis.

The data in the following sale-resale example (Table 5.3) comes from an apartment sales data set for Denver, Colorado. Between 1997 and 2002, 39 apartment properties were sold and resold in the market. The average year of the more recent sale was 2001 and the average year of the previous sale was 1998, meaning that the average sale gap was three years.

Table 5.3	Apartment Sales (1997–2002)				
Property Address	Number of Units	Resale Amount	Resale Date	Previous Sale Amount	Previous Closing Date
1010 E. 13th Ave.	44	$59,090	2002	$50,000	2001
970 Pearl St.	16	$66,562	2002	$45,703	2000
999 Ogden St.	67	$116,417	2002	$80,597	1999
224-238 Galapago St.	5	$75,000	2002	$52,000	1999
1415 Pearl St.	12	$62,500	2002	$45,833	1999
1350 Ogden St.	8	$85,000	2002	$43,750	1999
1220 Emerson St.	13	$59,615	2002	$44,615	1999
960 Pearl St.	16	$64,375	2002	$39,625	1998
1145 Sherman St.	48	$37,218	2002	$21,042	1998
900-910 E. 12th Ave.	26	$61,538	2001	$35,384	2000
1226 Marion St.	12	$50,000	2001	$35,416	2000
1085 Pearl St.	24	$87,500	2001	$64,583	2000
49 S. Pearl St.	12	$79,166	2001	$60,416	1999
222 Logan St.	34	$65,441	2001	$47,367	1999
195 S. Pennsylvania St.	23	$70,000	2001	$41,086	1999
1325 Corona St.	14	$57,857	2001	$27,142	1999
830 E. 11th Ave.	17	$67,647	2001	$32,813	1998
250 Pearl St.	29	$75,517	2001	$51,724	1998
236 S. Logan St.	20	$60,000	2001	$30,000	1998
20 S. Pennsylvania St.	12	$61,666	2001	$42,500	1997
985 Corona St.	12	$61,666	2000	$35,416	1999
955 Washington St.	8	$79,375	2000	$48,750	1999
789 Clarkson St.	58	$79,310	2000	$65,215	1999
787 Corona St.	5	$100,000	2000	$90,400	1999
1201 Clarkson St.	38	$46,052	2000	$31,578	1999
1125 Washington St.	43	$58,837	2000	$40,697	1999
1055 Clarkson St.	12	$51,666	2000	$31,833	1998
800 Emerson St.	25	$53,600	2000	$33,480	1997
600 Pennsylvania St.	53	$73,584	2000	$54,716	1997
43 Sherman St.	13	$50,000	2000	$28,076	1997
23 Clarkson St.	6	$68,333	2000	$45,000	1997
1148 Washington St.	9	$70,000	2000	$31,666	1997
66 Pearl St.	31	$54,645	1999	$51,677	1998
245 Bannock St.	15	$48,666	1999	$34,667	1998
155 S. Pennsylvania St.	34	$44,117	1999	$31,259	1998
63-69 Logan St.	12	$38,333	1999	$28,333	1997
1372 Marion St.	15	$53,333	1999	$25,000	1997
1285 Clarkson St.	25	$42,800	1999	$28,400	1997
1269 Marion St.	16	$32,187	1999	$27,812	1997
Mean Average	23	$63,298	2001	$42,451	1998

The average resale price per unit was $63,298, while it was $42,451 per unit for the prior sale. Using an unsophisticated approach results in the following calculation for the estimated average annual market trend for these properties:

Average Sale Price per Unit	Average Year
$63,298	2001
− $42,451	− 1998
$20,847	3
Annual change	$20,847 / 3 = $6,949
Percentage change	$6,949 / $42,451 = 16.4% per year

The statistical test to determine whether this difference is significant, the *paired t-test*, is similar to the independent t-test. As its name implies, this procedure compares two values for each property. In this case, the variables compared are the prices of the paired sales. Table 5.4 summarizes the descriptive and inferential statistics for the data set. The first box provides the mean average price for both sale sets. The second box analyzes the mean difference between both sales for all 40 properties. The histogram in Figure 5.6 illustrates the mean difference in price between the two sales for each property.

Table 5.4 and Figure 5.6 indicate that there is a significant difference between the paired sales when examining all 40 sales. The problem with this approach concerns the sales intervals, as well as the lack of time-specific analysis. The time difference between each paired sale ranges from 1 to 4 years. The

Table 5.4 Paired Samples Analysis

Paired Samples Statistics

		Mean	N	Std. Deviation	Std. Error Mean
Pair 1	Resale	$63,297.77	40	$16,766.421	$2,651.004
	Previous sale	$42,450.54	40	$14,755.915	$2,333.115

Paired Samples Test

		Paired Differences							
					95% Confidence Interval of the Difference				
		Mean	Std. Deviation	Std. Error Mean	Lower	Upper	t	df	Sig. (2-tailed)
Pair 1	Resale − Previous sale	$20,847.23	$8,755.342	$1,384.341	$18,047.14	$23,647.32	15.059	39	.000

Figure 5.6 **Mean Difference Between Sales**

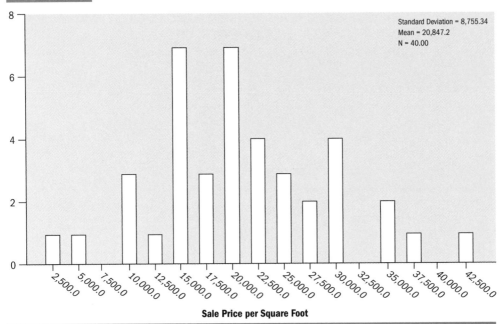

Standard Deviation = 8,755.34
Mean = 20,847.2
N = 40.00

Sale Price per Square Foot

average difference is 2.2 years, which results in an average annual difference of $9,476. The adjustment amount assumes a constant rate of change for all time periods. It also assumes that there have been no significant changes made to each apartment property between sales. If, for example, an extensive renovation occurs between sales, then the difference in the sale prices could be a result of the changes in the condition of the property, *not* solely changing market conditions.

Figure 5.7 shows each sale as an individual data point over time. Both the data spread for each year and the orange Lowess line indicate that the price per unit of apartment properties clearly leveled off after 2000. The scatter plot from SPSS clearly indicates a pattern that would be difficult or impossible to derive using a paired sales analysis.

While the paired t-test has excellent applicability in certain analyses, such as in a before-and-after analysis in medical research, in real estate analysis it has limited use. This is largely due to the limitations of paired sales analysis, which assumes away too much of market reality. Unless absolutely necessary, paired sales analysis should be avoided in favor of other, more defensible techniques. From a whole market perspective, it is truly a procedure of last resort.

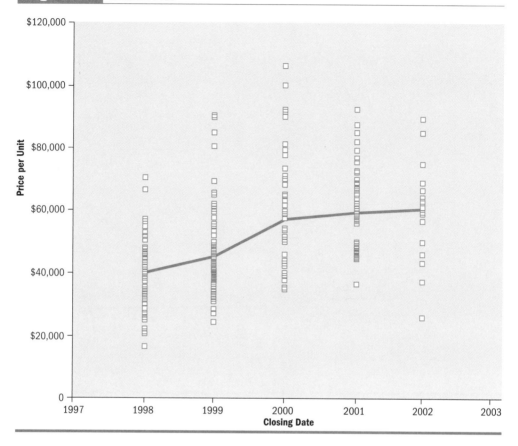

Figure 5.7 Scatter Plot

Case Study 3: Deriving Adjustments for Scale

Most of the time, it is assumed that larger quantities of an attribute result in a diminished value per unit. This expectation is based on economic principles of the Austrian school, which use marginal analysis to determine economic productivity. For example, if the unit of comparison is the sale price per square foot, then larger comparable properties would likely have a lower price per square foot than smaller properties of the same class. One of the previous examples, in fact, illustrated this, as shown in Figure 5.8.

The Lowess line indicates that there is an overall decline in the sale price per square foot based on the scale (i.e., size) of the improvement. The trend is non-linear, meaning that the best fit to the data is not a straight line but a curved line, as indicated in the figure. For buildings over 20,000 square feet, there does not appear to be any meaningful trend. Again, the variation around the trend line is due to variables

Lowess lines are trend lines based on a statistical weighting of the individual data points. They are used to check for bends in data trend lines, which may indicate non-linear relationships. A non-linear relationship would *not* be best represented by a straight line.

Figure 5.8 Industrial Sale Data Set (Lowess Line)

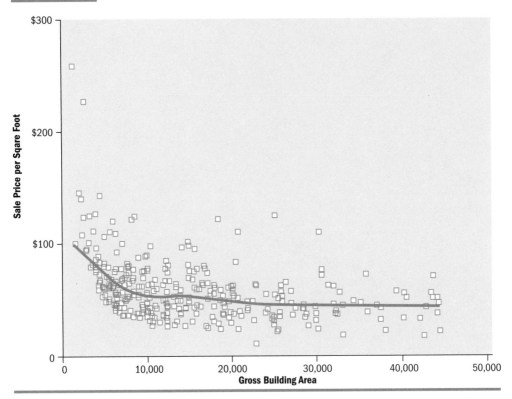

not included in this analysis or to unexplained variation (i.e., statistical noise).

A closer examination of the data indicates that a segmented linear trend line closely approximates the statistically derived Lowess line, as shown in Figure 5.9. The appraiser can next apply a manual adjustment based on the position of the comparable property versus the position of the subject. For example, if the subject property is 25,000 square feet and a comparable sale is 10,000 square feet, then the appraiser can approximate the adjustment by using the second segment of the orange trend line in Figure 5.9, as shown in Figure 5.10.

Based on the orange trend line in Figure 5.10, the 10,000 square foot rate of $55 per square foot is compared to the subject's 25,000 square foot rate of approximately $46 per square foot. The ratio of $55/$46, or 1.20, is an approximate 20% downward adjustment for scale between the comparable property and the subject. Please note that the $55 to $46 per square foot spread is used only as a reference point for the subject to adjust for scale. The final unit

Figure 5.9 Industrial Sale Data Set (Linear Trend Line)

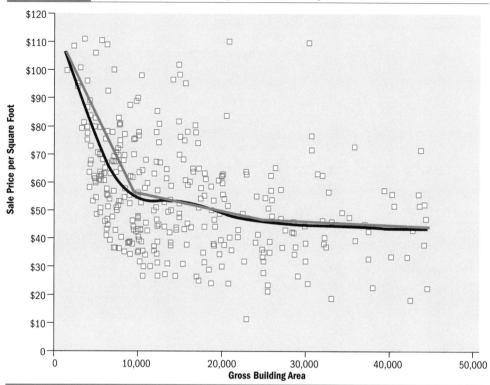

Figure 5.10 Industrial Sale Data Set (Closeup)

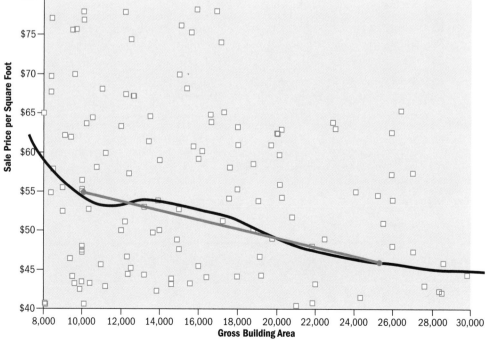

value for the subject would depend on the other adjustments applied as well as the scale adjustment.

The examples described above and in the Excel sidebar below are certainly defensible and make appraisal sense. Further statistical verification using SPSS yields statistical support for the significance of this adjustment. Using the Linear Regression routine (with **Improved Area** as the independent variable

Using Excel

Graphic analysis of the industrial data set used SPSS graphics routines to create the scatter plot and Lowess line and develop a manual adjustment for scale. The same analysis can be easily performed in Excel. After the industrial sales data was arrayed by improved area, a new variable, **Sale Price per Square Foot**, was created by dividing the sale price by the improved area. In Excel, this variable was inserted to the right of **Improved Area**. Next, the rows between 8,000 square feet up to 30,000 square feet were highlighted with the mouse. The Insert Chart command was selected, using the Scatter Plot option. Following the Chart Wizard steps in Excel created the chart shown below.

Excel Chart of Industrial Properties

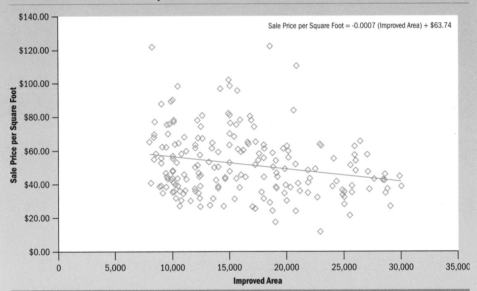

The trend line indicates a similar pattern to the Lowess line manually sketched in the example. As part of the Trend Line option in Excel, the equation for the trend line is automatically displayed. With an adjustment from the previous example for a 10,000-sq.-ft. comparable property, the scale adjustment for the 25,000-sq.-ft. subject property would be calculated as follows:

Comparable Property
$63.74 − 0.0007 × (10,000 sq. ft.) = $56.74

Subject Property
$63.74 − 0.0007 × (25,000 sq. ft.) = $46.24

Recall that manual analysis yielded very similar rates of $46 and $55 for the comparable property and subject property respectively. The final step would involve the same step used in the example using SPSS, dividing $55 by $46, which results in an adjustment ratio of 1.20.

Table 5.5   **SPSS Output**

Model Summary

Model	R	R-Square	Adjusted R-Square	Standard Error of the Estimate
1	.277ª	.052	.947	$18.70370
		A		B

Coefficients

Model	Unstandardized Coefficients		Standardized Coefficients	t	Sig.
	B	Standard Error	Beta		
1 (Constant)	63.7392	3.865		16.493	.000
Imp. Area	-.000737	.000	-.227	-3.264	.001
					C

a. Predictors: (Constant), Imp. Area

and **Sale Price per Square Foot** as the dependent variable) in SPSS results in the output shown in Table 5.5.

The model summary indicates the overall fit of this model, with an R-square of 0.052 (box A) and a standard error of $18.70 per square foot (box B). The coefficients box provides the output coefficients from the model under the column labeled B. The constant value is 63.7392, which is converted to dollars and rounded to $63.74 per square foot. The value below the constant is the adjustment for scale, or -0.000737. This is also converted and rounded to -$0.0007. These are exactly the same coefficient values derived from the Excel analysis. Additional statistical information is provided in box C, which indicates that the significance of the adjustment for scale is 0.001. As explained earlier, statistical significance is a test that measures the chance that the coefficient value is due to random chance—i.e., that there is no real relationship between the sale price per square foot and building size. In this instance, the 0.001 significance indicates that the chances are about 1 in 1,000 that this relationship is spurious.

What is an acceptable risk level for real estate valuation analysis? There is no answer. A 1% chance of error is probably more than sufficient for this type of analysis; in fact, this threshold could probably be raised to 5% or 10%, given that many of the relationships in real estate valuation have been extensively analyzed and are known.

A significance threshold of 1% is more than enough for real estate models; it would not be acceptable for "life and death" applications in medical science or engineering. Would anyone want to fly on an aircraft with a failure rate of 1%?

Case Study 4: Deriving Adjustments for Condition

Condition adjustments typically involve ordinal-level data. This data is termed *qualitative data*, because it is often based on judgment. Condition can be presented as a scale variable (such as excellent, good, average, fair, and poor) or it can be expressed as an effective year amount or as a percentage-good ratio. The example used in this case study is a coding scheme employing the following labels:

Numeric Code	Label
1	Excellent
2	Good
3	Average
4	Fair
5	Poor

Using the industrial data set from Chapter 4, the frequency distribution in Table 5.6 was developed. Using box and whisker plots (Figure 5.11) can help the appraiser compare the median sale price per square foot as well as the distribution for all five categories.

As noted earlier, the shaded box in a box and whisker plot indicates the spread of data between the twenty-fifth percentile and the seventy-fifth percentile, with the orange line within the box indicating the median sale price per square foot for each building condition category. The circles and corresponding number indicate extreme values within each condition category. Examining the differences between each category reveals some interesting findings. First, the two upper categories, **Excellent** and **Good**, appear to have nearly identical median values

Table 5.6	Frequency Distribution for Building Condition

Bldgcond

		Frequency	Percent	Valid Percent	Cumulative Percent
Valid	Excellent	21	4.8	4.8	4.8
	Good	64	14.6	14.6	19.4
	Average	322	73.3	73.3	92.7
	Fair	27	6.2	6.2	98.9
	Poor	5	1.1	1.1	100.0
	Total	439	100.0	100.0	

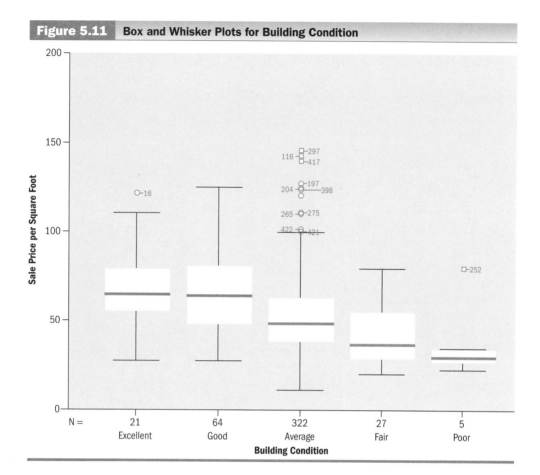

Figure 5.11 Box and Whisker Plots for Building Condition

and variances. Based on this similarity, it is reasonable to combine these two categories into a single category labeled **Above-average**. The lower two categories were also grouped into a single **Below-average** category. Other options would have been to leave the five categories as they are or to drop all properties in the **Poor** category, particularly if the subject property is in the **Average** or **Above-average** category. Often the extreme categories (i.e., those at either end of the spectrum) can be omitted if the subject is two or more categories away.

Combining the upper two and lower two categories results in the box and whisker plot in Figure 5.12. The recoded condition categories appear at first glance to be distinct. At this point appraisers could assume that they are in fact distinct enough to perform a simple comparison of the mean or median values between the three groups to derive adjustments. Assuming the subject property is in average condition, the goal is to develop an adjustment for properties in above-average condition and another

Individual categories should have at least 10 sales and should not overlap other categories too significantly. Of course, the statistical tests employed will check for just that, but appraisers can save some analysis time with visual inspection of the data.

Figure 5.12 | **Recoded Building Condition**

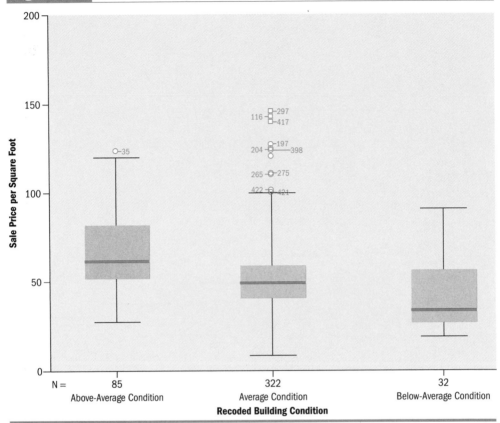

adjustment for properties in below-average condition. Table 5.7 compares the mean and median averages for all three groups.

The mean and median averages in Table 5.7 were derived using SPSS; a similar table could have been created using Excel. The appraiser could have even created a manual table, but this would be cumbersome because there are 439 sales to sort and tabulate by hand. Using the totals from Table 5.7 as follows creates manual adjustment factors that could be used in any adjustment grid:

	Adjustment for Above-Avg. Condition	Adjustment for Below-Avg. Condition
Median sale price per square foot	$63.80	$35.46
Median sale price per square foot (average condition)	$48.98	$48.98
Ratio	1.30257	0.7240
Adjustment (rounded)	-30%	+28%*

* Calculated by subtracting 0.7240 from 1.0 and rounding

Table 5.7 Mean and Median Comparison

Report

SPSF

Recoded Building	N	Mean	Median
Above-average condition	85	$67.17	$63.80
Average condition	322	$53.79	$48.98
Below-average condition	32	$47.92	$35.46
Total	439	$55.95	$51.25

The adjustments are calculated by dividing the median sale price per square foot of the above- and below-average properties by the median sale price per square foot of properties in average condition. The median value was used as opposed to the mean value because of the relative variance of the properties in below-average condition and the outliers in the other two categories. The calculations address the mechanics of applying ratio adjustments, assuming the subject is in average condition. The appraiser could choose to exclude all properties not in average condition, but this determination needs to be applied on a case-by-case basis.

In terms of statistical rigor, the analysis described assumes that there is a significant difference between the three ordered groups of industrial sales. The order does make appraisal sense, given that properties in above-average condition should sell for more than average properties, and properties in below-average condition should sell for less. Suppose, however, that further proof is needed. Perhaps the distributions are not as neatly differentiated, or the appraisal is to be used in court against another appraisal. In the first case study, the statistical test of choice was the t-test, which compared two groups of data. In this case study, three groups are being compared for significant differences. Fortunately, there is a similar statistical test called *analysis of variance* (ANOVA, for short) that is useful in situations where t-test analysis would not be used. In ANOVA analysis, like the t-test, the mean and distribution are compared to one another on a ratio basis, using statistical tables. Also like the t-test, the preferred mechanism to compute these statistics is a statistical software package such as SPSS.

The output shown in Table 5.8 uses ANOVA to determine the statistical significance of the three condition categories established earlier. Note the similarity of the output with the t-test. The first box provides a statistical description of the three categories as well as the entire sales data set: the mean sale price per square foot, the standard deviation of the mean, and the standard error, among other statistics. The third statistic, the standard error of the mean, is a measure that combines the standard deviation of the category with the square root of the number of values in that category. For the first category, the properties in below-average condition, the standard deviation of $22.79 per square foot is divided by the square root of the number of properties in this category (85), or 9.22, resulting in a standard error of $2.47. The confidence intervals of each category are calculated by multiplying the standard error by a factor of 2 on either side of the mean. Again, the purpose of this probability development is to test whether these categories are statistically different.

The second box tests whether the variances of the three categories are equal; the significance of 0.356 indicates that there is a 36% probability that at least one of the categories has a different distribution than the others. The third box shows the results of the

Table 5.8   ANOVA Output

Descriptives

SPSF

	N	Mean	Std. Deviation	Std. Error	95% Confidence Interval for Mean		Min	Max	Between Component Variance
					Lower Bound	Upper Bound			
Above-average condition	85	67.16	22.79	2.47	62.25	72.08	27.44	125.00	
Average condition	321	53.25	21.80	1.22	50.86	55.65	11.34	145.83	
Below-average condition	31	41.13	17.65	3.17	34.66	47.61	20.17	80.00	
Total	437	55.10	22.70	1.09	52.97	57.24	11.34	145.83	
Model Fixed effects			21.74	1.04	53.06	57.14			
Random effects				7.77	21.68	88.52			101.745

Test of Homogeneity of Variances

SPSF

Levene Statistic	df1	df2	Sig.
1.036	2	434	.356

ANOVA

SPSF

	Sum of Squares	df	Mean Square	F	Sig.
Between groups	19512.141	2	9756.071	20.636	.000
Within groups	205185.1	434	472.777		
Total	224697.2	436			

ANOVA analysis. As with the t-test, this statistical method creates a ratio (the F statistic) that is measured in a statistical table for significance. As with all of the other significance tests, the interpretation is based on the probability that the difference observed is due to random chance (i.e., that this is no real difference between the groups). In this case, the probability that the differences between the three groups are spurious is near zero.

ANOVA creates the F statistic by comparing the variance within a group to the variance between each group. Recall that the variance is simply the average squared difference between the mean of the group and each individual value. The within group mean square is calculated by multiplying the variance by the number of values within the group less one. The between group mean square is computed by subtracting the overall mean from the mean of each category, squaring the difference, and then multiplying this by the number of cases in each group. The following calculations were made for the industrial example:

Within group sum of squares = (standard deviation)^2 × (no. of values for each group less one) then add:

Below-average	$17.65^2 \times (31 - 1) =$	9,346
Average	$21.8^2 \times (321 - 1) =$	152,077
Above-average	$22.79^2 \times (85 - 1) =$	43,628
Total		205,051

Between group sum of squares = (overall mean − group mean)^2 × (no. of values) then add:

Below-average	$(41.13 - 55.10)^2 \times 31 =$	6,050
Average	$(53.25 - 55.10)^2 \times 321 =$	1,099
Above-average	$(67.16 - 55.10)^2 \times 85 =$	12,363
Total		19,512

The final step to calculate the F statistic is to divide the **Within group sum of squares** by the total number of sales less the number of categories less one (436 − (3 − 1) = 434), and then to divide the **Between group sum of squares** total by the total number of categories less one (3 − 1 = 2). The following computes the F statistic:

F statistic = (19,512/2) / (205,051/434) = 9,756/472 = 20.66

The F value is tested against the statistics table for significance. In this case, it is significant and tells us that at least one mean is significantly different from the others. To test for which means are different,

Table 5.9	Post Hoc Analysis Output						
(I) Recoded Building Condition	**(J) Recoded Building Condition**	**Mean Difference (I – J)**	**Std. Error**	**Sig.**	**95% Confidence Interval**		
					Lower Bound	**Upper Bound**	
Above-average cond.	Average condition	13.9108*	2.65234	.000	7.5364	20.2851
	Below-average cond.	26.0299*	4.56212	.000	15.0658	36.9940
Average condition	Above-average cond.	-13.9108*	2.65234	.000	-20.2851	-7.5364
	Below-average cond.	12.1192*	4.08946	.010	2.2910	21.9473
Below-average cond.	Above-average cond.	-26.0299*	4.56212	.000	-36.9940	-15.0658
	Average condition	-12.1192*	4.08946	.010	-21.9473	-2.2910

* The mean difference is significant at the .05 level.

ANOVA uses a procedure known as *post hoc analysis*. Table 5.9 was run in SPSS as part of ANOVA, using the Bonferroni post hoc procedure. This table provides statistical evidence that all of the categories for condition are significantly different from one another (under the shaded column). Once significance is proven, then the adjustment process can proceed as before, using the mean or median values for each category derived from the statistical analysis.

The ANOVA procedures shown in this example are complex, particularly if performed manually. Appraisers do not need to understand all of the theories behind the statistical procedures used, but they do need to understand how to apply the procedures. In this instance, ANOVA does allow appraisers to compare differences for nominal- and ordinal-level data, using the sale price (or sale price per square foot) as the dependent variable (a ratio-level variable). ANOVA cannot be used with two ordinal or nominal variables, but in the vast majority of cases, appraisers can use it to test a nominal- or ordinal-level variable against sale price (or, again, sale price per square foot).

Remember that the t-test procedure can be used to test for differences between two groups, while ANOVA performs the same type of testing for multiple groups. These procedures are valid comparison techniques, although the use of a complete valuation model using regression analysis that can simultaneously compare all the variables for significant effects on the dependent variable is a highly recommended alternative. Appraisers need to weigh the need to statistically test for significant differences. In many cases, the appraisal analysis does not require a full-blown ANOVA analysis.

CHAPTER 6

Market Trending Applications

"Time is never reasonable. Time is our enemy, Caesar."
—Elizabeth Taylor, *Cleopatra* (1963)

"I ain't got time to bleed . . ."
—Jesse Ventura, *Predator* (1987)

Time is often the most troublesome and perplexing variable in the valuation process. For real estate appraisers, time is a moving target for a variety of reasons:

- It varies in meaning and importance from assignment to assignment.
- It has a unique place in the adjustment process. The time adjustment is made after the adjustment for expenditures made immediately after purchase and prior to adjustments for physical attributes.
- It is directly addressed in USPAP. The sales history must be reported at least three years back for both residential and commercial properties.
- The valuation factor called *time* is not really about the passage of time anyway.

As it is understood and analyzed by appraisers, the **Time** variable, whose value is calculated in units like days, months, or years, is not a measure of temporal change but rather an indicator of relevant change in the marketplace.

Standard appraisal practice requires that changes in market conditions over the period of time between the dates of sale of comparable properties and the effective date of the appraisal must be accounted for in any appraisal. These changes are often reflected in the general price level for real estate and are referred to as *inflation* or *deflation*, depending on the direction of change. Although this factor is often labeled *time trending*, the label can be misleading. A more accurate term is *market trending*.

These marketwide changes in price level are created when there is an imbalance in the supply of and demand for real estate and when changes in economic conditions are brought about by external factors (war, tax laws, natural disasters, etc.). Market trending adjustments *do not* include changes in property attributes. In addition, the changes in general market conditions over time are not *caused* by time; the time period is simply a benchmark to measure such effects. It is vital that the appraiser is able to separate these effects. Fortunately, there are several well-established and straightforward methods to perform this analysis.

As noted earlier, changes in market conditions are considered prior to differences in location, physical attributes, and economic attributes between the subject and comparable sale properties. In the sales comparison approach, the market conditions adjustment is also generally considered after property rights conveyed, conditions of sale, financing and cash equivalency, and expenditures made immediately after the sale. The use of multiple regression and other multivariate models can make this point less critical, given that time trending can be included in models that measure differences simultaneously in physical and economic attributes.

For decades assessment appraisers have focused on the issue of market trending. Legislative requirements have formalized this, but even before such mandates, assessors considered market trending in their appraisal analyses. The nature of property taxation is typically time-constrained. Assessment appraisers are required to value all properties in a jurisdiction as of a given date and to use sales data from a specified sales period prior to that date. Changes in the economy during that sales period have brought about the need to identify and analyze the impact of such changes over time. In markets where the economic conditions are fairly constant, the analysis can be less specific and detailed. This is true in both fee appraisal and assessment appraisal. When conditions are not stable (e.g., constantly appreciating, depreciating, or both), then the issue of proper time adjustment analysis is critical.

Fee appraisers have traditionally used simple methods to account for market trending. These have ranged from paired sales analysis to anecdotal reporting of prevailing real estate price level changes, as reported by sources such as governmental agencies and real estate brokers. This was typically done

Market trending adjustments are required by USPAP under Standards Rule 1-3, which concerns identifying and analyzing economic supply and demand as well as market area trends. Without a clear understanding of these changes over time, particularly between the date of the market data and the effective date of the appraisal, the appraiser simply cannot perform a competent appraisal analysis.

in an atmosphere of few sales and limited analytical resources. With more abundant data and requirements to analyze all relevant market data, fee appraisers today face what assessment appraisers faced years ago. The major difference today is that the analytical tools and valuation theories are much more advanced than those available during the 1980s and 1990s. Market trend analysis offers methods that fee appraisers can readily apply in their everyday appraisal practice. Some of these methods come directly from the assessment branch of appraisal, although fee appraisal applications may require less precision.

Examining the Data

To analyze market trending effectively, the data needs to be correctly arrayed. To do this the appraiser needs to first determine the appropriate sales period, usually indicated by the earliest sale date and the effective date of the appraisal. Other endpoints can be used, if they make appraisal sense. The sales period is determined based on these beginning and ending dates. A longer sales period usually means that the measure of time (days, months, years, etc.) can be a larger increment. For example, for a six-month sales period, transactions would likely be arrayed by the month of sale or perhaps the day of sale. They could even be arrayed by the sale quarter (i.e., a three-month block), which would result in the data being displayed in one of two quarters. It would *not* make sense to array sales data by the year of sale because the unit of measure spans a greater period of time than the sales period. On the other hand, for a sales period of five years, using the month or day of sale as the unit of measure could be *too* precise. The unit of measure used should make appraisal sense.

The next step involves coding the data based on the sales period and the *number* of units (i.e., days, months, quarters, years). A simple coding scheme, using the effective date of the appraisal as the zero period, can be entered on a spreadsheet or calculated as a new variable in SPSS, MiniTab, or another statistical software package. One conceptual issue an analyst must address concerns the coding of the sales periods in reverse order. This allows observers to read from past periods toward the present when reading from left to right.

Table 6.1 illustrates several coding schemes using different units of measurement for an 18-month period between June 1, 2001, and November

	Unit of Measure			
Table 6.1 **Age Coding**				
Sale Month	**Monthly**	**Quarterly**	**Biannual**	**Annual**
June 2001	17	5	2	1
July 2001	16	5	2	1
August 2001	15	5	2	1
September 2001	14	4	2	1
October 2001	13	4	2	1
November 2001	12	4	2	0
December 2001	11	3	1	0
January 2002	10	3	1	0
February 2002	9	3	1	0
March 2002	8	2	1	0
April 2002	7	2	1	0
May 2002	6	2	1	0
June 2002	5	1	0	0
July 2002	4	1	0	0
August 2002	3	1	0	0
September 2002	2	0	0	0
October 2002	1	0	0	0
November 2002	0	0	0	0

11, 2002 (the effective date of the appraisal). Note that as the units of measure go from monthly to quarterly to biannual to annual, the sales data becomes less precise. This is not necessarily undesirable. The use of an annual sales period can sometimes negate the effects of seasonality, which reflect cyclical trends within a given year.

Once the sales period coding is complete, the sales data can be graphed or placed in a table for further analysis. Generally, the sales data is expressed per unit of measure, such as the sale price per square foot (used for industrial and commercial properties), sale price per unit (for multifamily and lodging properties), or sale price per lot (for residential and commercial subdivisions). The unit of measure selected must make appraisal sense and will ultimately be used in the sales comparison approach. While it is possible to use a different unit of comparison for the market trend analysis than the unit used in the overall valuation model, the transformation from the former to the latter can be complex.

In Table 6.2 a quarterly unit of measure is applied to the average sale price per square foot for the industrial data set described in previous chapters. While the table uses a summary value for the sale price (i.e., the mean monthly sale price per square foot),

Table 6.2	Industrial Sales by Quarter	
Sale Month	Quarter	Mean Sale Price per Square Foot
June 2001	5	$50.33
July 2001	5	$50.45
August 2001	5	$52.34
September 2001	4	$53.45
October 2001	4	$54.01
November 2001	4	$54.50
December 2001	3	$54.90
January 2002	3	$55.61
February 2002	3	$54.99
March 2002	2	$55.93
April 2002	2	$56.25
May 2002	2	$56.75
June 2002	1	$57.89
July 2002	1	$57.03
August 2002	1	$58.03
September 2002	0	$58.25
October 2002	0	$58.99
November 2002	0	$59.45

note that the analysis ignores inter-quartile differences. In other words, for Quarter 1, which spans September 2002 to November 2002, the trend between months is ignored. A sale occurring in early September 2002 gets the same code as a sale occurring in late November 2002. While this may be acceptable or even desirable in certain instances, it is important that the appraiser be aware of this loss in information. Figure 6.1 depicts this quarterly sales analysis.

The graph shows clearly the slight decline in the sale price per square foot of these industrial sales over the nine months prior to the effective date of the appraisal (Quarters 0, 1, and 2). Compare this chart to Figure 6.2, which displays the same data using the sale month instead of the sale quarter across the x-axis. Again, it is important for the appraiser to understand what is gained and lost from using different units of measure. Other considerations include seasonal factors, changes in the observed trend (i.e., splining, which will be explained shortly), and the distribution of the sales data.

Seasonal factors affect different property types in different markets at different rates. In other words, the appraiser needs to understand the attributes of the property class being appraised and the market

Figure 6.1   **Sales of All Properties**

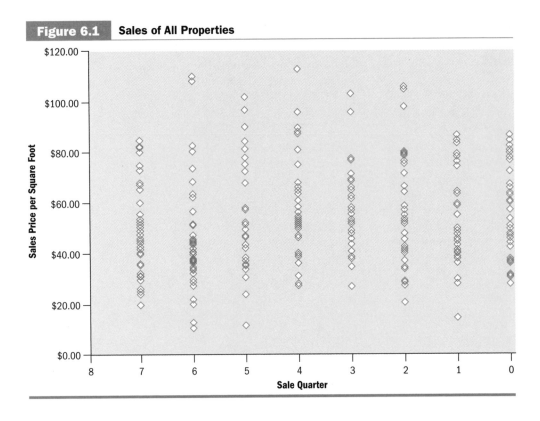

Figure 6.2   **Sale Price per Square Foot by Sale Month**

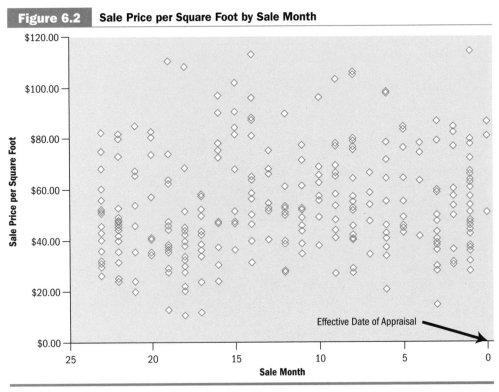

where it is being appraised. A lodging property located next to Denver International Airport, for example, will be affected differently by seasonal factors than a lodging property located in the core area of Vail Village, Colorado. If the goal is to determine an annual market trend adjustment, then seasonal trends must be accounted for. This can be done by comparing the same quarter for different sale years–e.g., January through March 2002 compared to January through March of 2001.

Market trends can change over the sales period. For example, in many markets real estate prices increased for the first half of 2001, leveled off for the latter half of 2001, and dropped slightly in 2002. Using a linear (i.e., straight-line) trend for this data could be inaccurate and misleading. This is prohibited under USPAP and needs to be accounted for analytically.

In Figure 6.3, the orange trend line is based on a model that included a splining function, while the black line is the linear trend line. Although the differences appear small, note that the orange trend line indicates a clear drop in value in the last three quarters, which are the most recent nine months of sales activity. The linear trend creates a potentially mis-

> Splining occurs when there is a change (or bend) in the observed market trend line. For example, this phenomenon occurred after September 11, 2001, in certain real estate markets. Property prices in many markets went from an appreciating trend to a level or even depreciating market trend. Charting this data would have indicated a splining that occurred on September 11, 2001.

| Figure 6.3 | Sale Price per Square Foot by Sale Quarter |

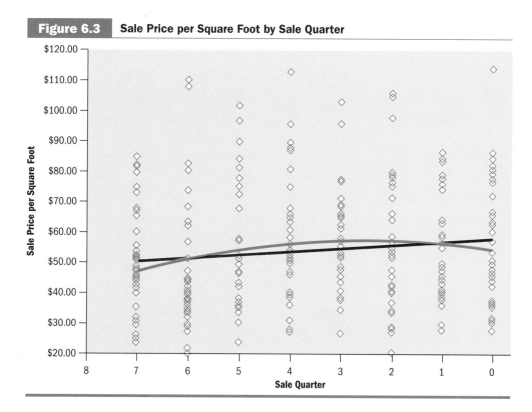

leading situation in which the general price level appears to be increasing over the entire 24-month sales period. What if the appraisal assignment included projecting the sales trend into the future? The two lines would result in significantly different projections.

A final concern is the distribution of data. This is a particularly significant concern for smaller data sets (less than 30 sales per year) but must be considered for all sets of data. Analyzing the spread of data points across the sales period can help identify bunching of data, where the sales cluster during a given interval. This pattern can unduly influence the overall market trend. For example, in a small mountain market in Colorado, the reported sales of 20 units in a single condominium project can significantly impact the sales trend analysis for the entire multifamily market. The appraiser must decide how to treat such sale clusters in the context of the whole market. If the majority of condominium sales are resales of existing condominium units that average five to 10 years in age, then the impact of these new sales can result in misleading time trend statistics. The appraiser using time trend analysis must not mistake changes in the distribution of properties sold for a secular inflation or deflation trend affecting all properties in that class. In this example, there is a risk that any time trend concluded could in fact be the impact of a cluster of new condominium sales in a predominantly resale housing market.

As noted previously, it is recommended that appraisers use either statistical or spreadsheet software to develop market trend models. Nevertheless, analyzing this data manually can reveal meaningful results. A simple array showing the percentage changes can be used to conclude an appropriate sales trend adjustment. Table 6.3, which shows monthly sales data for an 18-month period, indicates a defensible time trend adjustment conclusion.

The percentage changes in Table 6.3 were based on the average sale price per square foot divided by the value for the previous sales period, moving in reverse order *up* the chart. Based on these reported changes from month to month, the sales trend appears to increase for the first six months, level off for the middle six months, and then decrease slightly for the last six months of the sales period up to the effective date. To calculate the specific adjustment

Table 6.3	Time Trend Adjustment		
Sale Month	**Sale Month**	**Average Sale Price per Square Foot**	**Avg. % Change over Previous Month**
June 2001	17	$105	–
July 2001	16	$109	4%
August 2001	15	$111	2%
September 2001	14	$114	3%
October 2001	13	$115	1%
November 2001	12	$118	3%
December 2001	11	$119	1%
January 2002	10	$119	0%
February 2002	9	$119	0%
March 2002	8	$118	-1%
April 2002	7	$118	0%
May 2002	6	$118	0%
June 2002	5	$116	-2%
July 2002	4	$114	-2%
August 2002	3	$112	-2%
September 2002	2	$112	0%
October 2002	1	$111	-1%
November 2002*	0	$111	0%

* Base month

factor between a given sale month and the base month, simply divide the sale month by the base month as follows:

Sale month	June 2001	$105
divided by		÷
Base month	November 2002	$111
equals		=
Adjustment factor		0.95

The sale price of a comparable property could be adjusted by *dividing* the sale price by 0.95 or multiplying the sale price by its reciprocal, 1.05.

Plotting data gives the reader even more readily digestible information regarding time trending, if the data is properly formatted. Convention usually places the time unit of measure along the x-axis and the unit of comparison (sale price per square foot, sale price per unit, etc.) along the y-axis. Typically all of the sales data points are displayed, even if there are hundreds, because a graph (unlike a table) can easily accommodate many points. Plotting just the mean or median data (such as the average sale price per square foot for a given month) is an option, but information is lost in the process. The two graphs in

Figures 6.4 and 6.5 indicate the market trend for the same data set. It is clear that the overall trends are similar, but much more information concerning the spread (i.e., distribution) of data in each month is provided by Figure 6.5. This can be important because any outliers can be readily detected in Figure 6.5, while Figure 6.4 masks these potentially problem sales by showing only the mean values per month.

In most spreadsheet software, the trend line can accommodate several functions, such as a linear trend or more complex non-linear forms. These other forms may help to identify whether there are changes or breakpoints in the data. In these cases, a straight-line trend is not appropriate. In Excel, for example, the trend line can take linear, logarithmic, power, exponential, polynomial, or moving average forms. Logarithmic, power, and exponential forms deal with increasing or decreasing changes or compounded change in the relationship. These forms should be used only when the appraiser fully understands the relationship involved. In most cases, a linear relationship will suffice, given that the linear trend is similar to these other forms over short intervals. The added statistical "fit" provided by more complex forms is more than offset by the added complexity of expressing the relationship between time and sale price. Polynomial and moving average forms can fit trends with multiple bends in them. The polynomial trend in particular can indicate changes in the time trend at multiple points.

Complex graphic analysis should only be used to identify *when* the sales trend appears to change; the actual quantified adjustment should be applied manually or modeled in a comprehensive regression model. An example of the former is covered later in this chapter; an example of the latter is presented in Chapter 8.

Measuring Market Trends

As noted previously, assessment appraisal has dealt with time trending for many years. Out of this field, four recommended approaches have been developed to analyze this data:

1. Unit value comparisons
2. Sales ratio trend analysis
3. Multiple regression analysis
4. Resale (paired sales) analysis

The approaches have varying applicability to fee appraisal, given the different goals of mass appraisal

Figure 6.4 Monthly Mean Sale Price by Sale Month

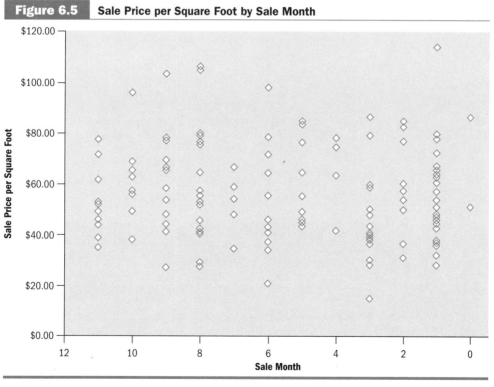

Figure 6.5 Sale Price per Square Foot by Sale Month

and single-property appraisal. Several of these approaches have been modified for fee appraisal practice with the understanding that the goal of most fee appraisals is a point estimate value of a single property.

If resources are limited (i.e., no spreadsheet software, lack of data), then paired sales, anecdotal, and survey methods are an appraiser's best bets. Unit value comparisons and ratio analyses are stronger analytical methods for determining and supporting market time trending. The unit value comparison method is preferred because that it can be performed without a computer. Ratio methods, while technically preferred over paired sales, anecdotal, and survey methods, are more problematic for fee appraisers.

Unit Value Comparisons

Unit value comparisons have already been covered in the earlier examples in this chapter. This type of market trend analysis plots the appropriate unit of comparison (such as sale price per square foot) over time.

Unit value comparison methods require that the appraiser array the data and examine it for any errors and outliers. This can be done either manually in a table or graphically in a spreadsheet. The appraiser needs to be cautious about what is being presented by the data. It is assumed that most of the change over time is due to changes in market conditions, not to changes in the data. If the sales data is distributed unevenly, such as when new sales are clustered in one time period, then the change over time may be caused by differences in the type of sale properties as opposed to general market conditions.

Sales Ratio Trend Analysis

Sales ratio trend analysis examines the ratio of the sale price to a base value. For the base value, assess-

Simple Methods of Measuring Market Trends

Anecdotal data includes market time trends reported by market experts such as government entities and real estate sources. Obviously, citing more sources strengthens this method so long as the sources generally agree as to the specific market time trend. In addition, the appraiser needs to exercise caution to identify and account for bias. Asking the local builders association for its opinion of the general price level of housing in a market may yield a more biased response than asking the local government planning department.

Survey methods to determine market time trending are offshoots of the anecdotal method with more clout. Using published data (even self-published data) is stronger than reporting individual opinions. Appraisers need to refer to recognized sources and again ascertain any potential bias from that source. Obviously, advertising data is suspect, while academic and vendor reports are generally less prone to bias. Sources subject to peer and professional review are preferred over sources that are published with limited or no review.

ment appraisers use their market value estimate as of a given date, usually the assessment date. For fee appraisers, finding a base value is more problematic. Assessed value could be used as a proxy for market value, but the variation in the market veracity (i.e., accuracy) is significant across jurisdictions in many states. Another base value could be the adjusted sale price (i.e., less any adjustments for time trending). Theoretically, the adjusted values would account for all other differences between the subject property and the comparable sale properties.

Using adjusted sale values from comparable sale properties limits the amount of sales data in most cases, unless the appraiser wants to prepare an adjustment grid with 30 sales. While sales ratio methods are very desirable for verifying modeling accuracy in fee appraisal modeling, their practical applications in performing analyses of market trending are limited at present to appraisers who have access to accurate county assessment valuations to use as the base variable. The methodology is simple, but the lack of a valid base variable in most instances renders this method impractical.

With both unit value comparisons and ratio analysis methods, the sales data can be summarized as either the mean or median sale price per time period (such as monthly median sale price). However, caution must be exercised since this involves ignoring the distribution of data per period. Ignoring individual sales means ignoring outlier sales, which can provide valuable information as to the strengths and weaknesses of the market trend analysis.

The trend from either the ratio or unit value can be tested for statistical significance. Limitations of these methods include the assumption that any significant change is due to market trends exclusively and not to differences in the subclass of properties sold during the sales period. For example, a general residential market trend model assumes that the same type and quality of residential product is sold throughout the sales period.

Multiple Regression Analysis

The third method of time trending analysis is *multiple regression modeling*, which includes market trending as a variable in the valuation model. The efficiency of the regression analysis allows for this variable to be tested while accounting for the other factors that can affect value, such as improvement attributes and location. In addition, regression allows the time trend to be segmented (i.e., broken up) into appropriate clusters in the event of splining. More advanced forms of regression can also test for changes in the time trend over the sales period using nonlinear formats.

The method to test for market time trending preferred by fee appraisers is the multiple regression modeling method. Using a regression-based statistical model allows the analyst to test for market trending while at the same time testing for location and property attribute differences. It requires more data (20 sales are a base minimum for most models) and a degree of skill from the appraiser. The ability to test for significance for market trending makes this approach superior to all others.

Multiple regression modeling also provides the most defensible analysis by quantifying the relationship between the subject and the comparable sales data, attribute by attribute. Not only can the effects of time trending be quantified, but its relative contribution to the valuation of the subject can be determined as well. The multiple regression model is presented in Chapter 8 and includes a market trend variable.

Resale (Paired Sales) Analysis

Finally, *resale analysis*, or paired sales analysis, allows the appraiser to test for time with limited data. The results of this type of analysis must be carefully evaluated. If a property sells more than once during the sales period, the difference is often interpreted as evidence of changes in the general price level of the market. To make this case, the appraiser must ensure that the resale property has not changed significantly between the sales dates and that both sales are bona fide market transactions. One weakness of this analysis is that the practice known as *flipping* (i.e., the illegal purchase and resale of property at an artificially inflated price) can skew the results, indicating sales appreciation when there is none. A general market trend claim based on the evidence of the resale of a single property is open to criticism. Is it reasonable to conclude a market trend for an entire class of properties based on the resale history of one property?

Appraisers can strengthen the results of paired sales analysis by using multiple paired sales. Artificial paired sales analysis can be conducted when two properties are sold during the sales period and they are extremely comparable to one another. The inference is that the sole difference between both properties is due to market trending.

Applying Market Time Trending Results

Generally, market trend adjustments come in the form of either whole value adjustments or percentage adjustments, depending on the method of derivation. In the case of unit value comparison and paired sales analysis, most applications of those methods yield percentage adjustments that can be applied to the comparable sale properties either prior to or within an adjustment grid.

Applying the adjustment is straightforward. Multiple regression output in an additive model generally expresses the time factor as a number rather than a percentage. Standard appraisal practice would indicate that the appraiser divide this number by the constant in the equation to arrive at a per-unit adjustment factor. The appraiser would then multiply this by the number of sale months to arrive at the adjustment for the comparable sale. The regression-based example illustrated by Figure 6.6 indicates how this works mechanically, using the industrial sales data set.

The trend shown in the chart is based on a linear regression model provided in Excel. As part of the Trend Line option, the equation can be placed in the graph. The format is

$$y = a + bx$$

with y representing the sale price per square foot, x representing the sale month, b representing the monthly trend, and a representing the value per square foot as of the effective date of the appraisal. Based on the reverse coding used to identify the sale month, the sign of the monthly trend needs to be reversed, so positive values become negative and vice versa. This becomes obvious by simply looking at Figure 6.6. For a sale occurring in month 10, the adjustment would have to be negative since the line slopes downward toward month 0, the current month. Using the equation for the trend line results in the adjustment calculations in Table 6.4.

The appraiser can adjust each comparable sale by either the whole dollar method or using a percentage adjustment. Again, remember that with a declining trend line the adjustments are negative, i.e., adjusted downward toward the subject. An appreciating trend line would require a positive adjustment, adjusted upward toward the subject. The model shown in Figure 6.7 helps to explain when to adjust up and when to adjust down.

Figure 6.6 Sale Price per Square Foot by Sale Month

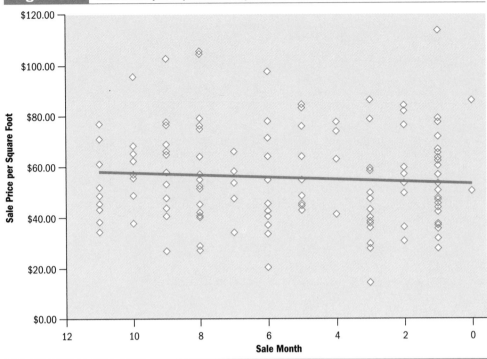

Table 6.4 Adjustment Calculations

Formula market trend adjustment = $53.80 − (sale month) × $0.42

Sale Month	Whole Dollar	Percentage
0	(0) × $0.42 = $0	$0 / $53.80 = 0%
1	(1) × $0.42 = $0.42	$0.42 / $53.80 = 0.1%
2	(2) × $0.42 = $0.84	$0.84 / $53.80 = 1.6%
3	(3) × $0.42 = $1.26	$1.26 / $53.80 = 2.3%
4	(4) × $0.42 = $1.68	$1.68 / $53.80 = 3.1%
5	(5) × $0.42 = $2.10	$2.10 / $53.80 = 3.9%
6	(6) × $0.42 = $2.52	$2.52 / $53.80 = 4.7%
7	(7) × $0.42 = $2.94	$2.94 / $53.80 = 5.5%
8	(8) × $0.42 = $3.36	$3.36 / $53.80 = 6.2%
9	(9) × $0.42 = $3.78	$3.78 / $53.80 = 7.0%
10	(10) × $0.42 = $4.20	$4.20 / $53.80 = 7.8%
11	(11) × $0.42 = $4.62	$4.62 / $53.80 = 8.6%

For example, if a sale occurs 10 months prior to the effective date of the appraisal, the following adjustments could be applied, assuming a comparable sale price of $67.00 per square foot:

	Whole Dollar Adjustment	Percentage Adjustment
Comparable sale	$67.00	$67.00
Adjustment	– $4.20	× 0.928
Adjusted unit value	$62.80	$62.18

Again, the adjustment can be either a percentage adjustment or a whole unit adjustment.

An alternative method to these manual adjustments involves a valuation model with market time adjustments expressed as one of the valuation factors. Although clients must be prepared to understand this new form of reporting values, the advantage of this method is that the appraiser can directly use the model coefficients from the regression analysis without having to translate the results into a manual adjustment grid. The equation is based entirely on the regression equation and output.

With a valuation model equation, the subject can be valued directly without the added step of introducing comparable properties adjusted to the sub-

---

Figure 6.7 **Positive and Negative Adjustments**

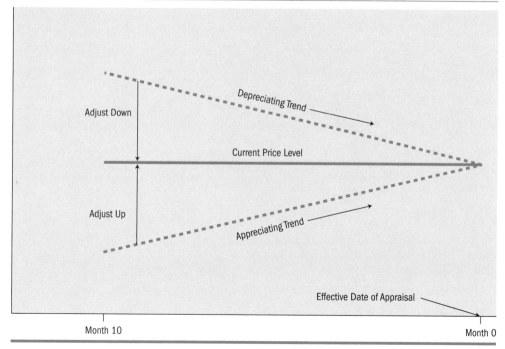

ject. The valuation equation represents a composite value equation that directly values the subject, based on its attributes. Chapter 8 presents this "best of all worlds" valuation procedure.

Splining

When the market trend analysis indicates that the general price level changes direction during the sales period, then a market trend *spline* is said to have occurred. As mentioned previously, *splining* simply means that the market trend line breaks or bends during the sales period. A simple but effective way to account for changes in market trending is to develop two sets of adjustments, based on two separate sales periods within the larger sales period.

For example, assume the sales period is identified as the 36 months prior to the effective date of the appraisal. Next, assume that inflation runs approximately 1% per month for the first 12 months of the sales period, is level for the next 12-month period, and then declines (i.e., deflation) for the last 12-month period. Since the effective date occurs at the end of this period, Figure 6.8 shows the overall market trend model in this example.

Using Table 6.5, the appraiser can apply manual adjustments based on the sale month using the cumulative adjustment column. For example, a sale in February 2000 would be adjusted upward by 5%. A comparable sale that was sold during February 2001 would be adjusted downward by 6%. These adjustments already account for the two changes in the market trend during the sales period.

Figure 6.8   **Overall Market Trend Model**

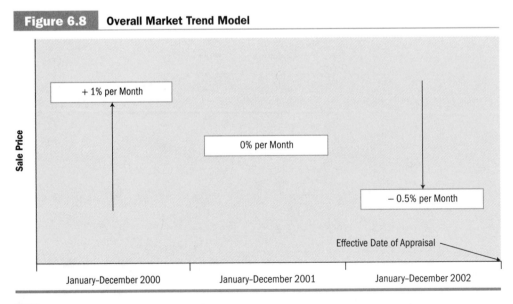

Table 6.5	Market Trend Adjustments		
Sale Month	Sale Month	Monthly Adjustment	Cumulative Adjustment
January 2000	36	1%	6.0%
February 2000	35	1%	5.0%
March 2000	34	1%	4.0%
April 2000	33	1%	3.0%
May 2000	32	1%	2.0%
June 2000	31	1%	1.0%
July 2000	30	1%	0.0%
August 2000	29	1%	-1.0%
September 2000	28	1%	-2.0%
October 2000	27	1%	-3.0%
November 2000	26	1%	-4.0%
December 2000	25	1%	-5.0%
January 2001	24	0%	-6.0%
February 2001	23	0%	-6.0%
March 2001	22	0%	-6.0%
April 2001	21	0%	-6.0%
May 2001	20	0%	-6.0%
June 2001	19	0%	-6.0%
July 2001	18	0%	-6.0%
August 2001	17	0%	-6.0%
September 2001	16	0%	-6.0%
October 2001	15	0%	-6.0%
November 2001	14	0%	-6.0%
December 2001	13	0%	-6.0%
January 2002	12	-0.5%	-6.0%
February 2002	11	-0.5%	-5.5%
March 2002	10	-0.5%	-5.0%
April 2002	9	-0.5%	-4.5%
May 2002	8	-0.5%	-4.0%
June 2002	7	-0.5%	-3.5%
July 2002	6	-0.5%	-3.0%
August 2002	5	-0.5%	-2.5%
September 2002	4	-0.5%	-2.0%
October 2002	3	-0.5%	-1.5%
November 2002	2	-0.5%	-1.0%
December 2002	1	-0.5%	-0.5%

CHAPTER 7
How to Mislead (i.e., Lie) With Statistics

"There are three types of lies: lies, damn lies, and statistics."

−variously attributed to Benjamin Disraeli, Alfred Marshall, Mark Twain, and others

Everyone knows the saying about lying with statistics and, almost 50 years after its publication, the book that introduced the phrase, *How To Lie With Statistics* by Darrell Huff, remains in print. For an appraiser, misleading the reader of an appraisal report with statistics, even when the misinformation is not directly related to the valuation of the subject property, is never appropriate. Not only should appraisers avoid such tricks of the statistical trade, but they also must be able to recognize such practices when evaluating analyses prepared by others. When an appraiser is called upon to judge an analysis or an entire AVM system, the data presentation and analysis must be verified and checked for misleading graphics or tables. The goal is to investigate the accuracy of another's analyses, not to be cynical about the use of statistics in general.

The following three techniques are tried-and-true methods of deception that use statistical analysis to further a point without regard for the truth:

- The avalanche
- The picture
- The confounder

Appraisers need to be aware of these methods of misdirection and deception because the appraiser's mission is to provide an unbiased analysis that is not misleading. Another part of the mission involves credibility. While USPAP provides some guidance, the appraisal profession is still in the process of developing specific guidelines. There remains a wide range of standards and practice regarding mass appraisal and statistical analysis in fee appraisal today.

The Avalanche

The avalanche method of deception involves overwhelming the reader with numbers. The appraiser simply presents a mountain of data with little or no correlation to the subject property. The goal of this intimidation technique is to provide so much data that the reader cannot begin to challenge or verify any conclusions. There may be no conclusions offered, in fact, but this can be obscured by the amount of data presented.

Users of this method prey on several human traits. First, simple pride often makes us accept data on a quantity basis, without questioning its veracity (i.e., whether it is relevant and accurate). A simple question such as "What does all this mean?" regarding the data mountain and market reality can quickly turn the mountain into a molehill. Unfortunately, such questions are seldom asked because the reader of the data does not want to appear ignorant.

As mentioned earlier, most of us can barely comprehend and manipulate five comparables sales. Thus, we cannot comprehend pages and pages and row upon row of data, particularly if no linkage to the subject property is demonstrated. To help their clients interpret and understand an avalanche of data presented to them, appraisers reviewing such data need to ask the following questions:

- What is the linkage to the subject?
- What are the conclusions?
- Where is the analysis?
- Where is the executive summary?

These simple questions can be very revealing. (Remember, raw data is not information.) Most of the voluminous data monsters an appraiser will encounter can be easily slayed with common-sense, appraisal-related questions.

The opposite can also be the case. A data avalanche can be implied, even though data is not presented. Some AVM practitioners, for example, like to suggest that behind every AVM value is a warehouse full of computers working to produce *the value*. They imply that because their statistical analyses are supported by large quantities of data and a great amount of computing power, they cannot be wrong. They love to whack experienced, professionally designated appraisers over the head with this technique, even when little if any supportive data is presented.

Both "avalanche" methods are forms of intimidation that valuation professionals need not worry about if they are properly prepared. Both violate USPAP and both say more about the veracity of the presenter than the intelligence of the reader. Remember that the real estate data is being analyzed for purposes of market valuation, not to develop the astrophysics to proceed on a mission to colonize Mars. All of the analysis must be presented in an understandable format because it must be understood by the reader. Frankly, it is *not* rocket science. In some instances market dynamics can be complex, but more often than not the situation is relatively straightforward. Presenting a trans-log function to determine the market value of metal-frame buildings in an industrial market is not only misleading under USPAP, it is plainly absurd. The appraiser faced with analytical overkill from another appraiser or an "expert" in the field of statistics needs to keep this in mind. What good is data analysis if the reader can't understand it? More critically, what may be hidden under the data mountain that could be misleading?

The Picture

Deceptive practices involving graphic presentations have been around since the first fake da Vinci painting was peddled on the streets of Venice. Oil and canvas have given way to modern computer-generated tables and graphics designed to influence viewers in unethical ways. The examples in this section are certainly not exhaustive, but the authors have personally witnessed all of these shady practices using computer-generated graphics.

Example 1: Painting Part of the Picture

In the hyperbolic commotion over the epidemic of low self-esteem among adolescent girls, "experts" have pointed out that adolescent girls are more likely to *attempt* suicide than adolescent boys. What they fail to mention is that adolescent boys actually *do* commit suicide at a greater rate than girls and that, overall, adolescent girls have better self-esteem than boys. In this case, proponents have presented only a portion of the picture. Other data, countering the proponents' position, is not provided. The reader is left with a partial, biased picture of "reality." The "trick" used here is reporting only a portion of the data available to make your case.

Table 7.1 presents a real estate corollary and illustrates a very effective way to lead the reader to a specific conclusion. The table suggests to the casual observer that job creation in a particular market is proceeding at a healthy pace into the twenty-first century. One might even conclude that this market is growing significantly. Adding a little more data to the table (see Table 7.2) makes the picture significantly less rosy. The labor force as a percentage of the total population is actually declining. In this market, job growth is *not* keeping pace with population growth; the market-adjusted rate actually indicates a general decline in employment.

Table 7.1	Job Growth
Year	Job Growth
1999	+1,200
2000	+900
2001	+1,000
2002	+1,200

Table 7.2	Job Growth and Decline of Workers as Percentage of Total Population	
Year	Job Growth	Employed Workers as a Percentage of Total Population
1999	+1,200	0.41
2000	+900	0.40
2001	+1,000	0.38
2002	+1,200	0.37

Many sources of Internet-based market data, particularly chambers of commerce and tourist boards, can paint a picture using only one color in the palette. The appraiser should consult more objective sources, such as local planning departments, for data. Getting data from more than one source and comparing data from different sources are good ways to paint the whole market picture.

Example 2: Marginalizing Data

Another great way to mislead is by manipulating the margins of a graph to magnify or otherwise distort relative differences between the data. While this is certainly an effective approach if the goal is to mislead, it really should be avoided because anyone who knows the trick can easily spot it.

The graph in Figure 7.1 implies that there are many more cars of type A on the road after five years than cars of other types. One is led to conclude that Car A is much more reliable than Car D. Figure 7.2 tells a different story, using the same data but *without* manipulating the y-axis.

Showing the whole margin from 0% to 100% on the y-axis describes the real situation. The vast major-

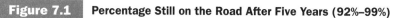

Figure 7.1 Percentage Still on the Road After Five Years (92%–99%)

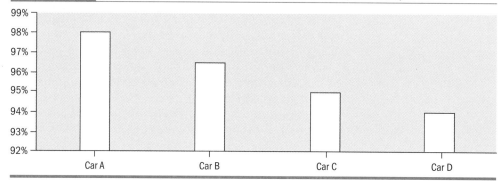

Figure 7.2 Percentage Still on the Road After Five Years (0%–100%)

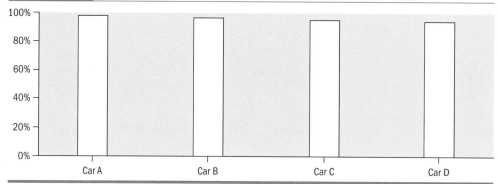

ity of all four brands of cars are on the road after five years. There are small (and probably insignificant) differences in the reliability of these car brands.

The preparer of Figure 7.1 has distorted the perception of reality by altering the y-axis margin and magnifying the perceived differences in the percentages of cars still on the road. Instead of presenting the entire range, only the upper 8% has been presented, implying that Car A is much more reliable than the other car types. Is the graph a lie? No. Is it misleading? Obviously. Figure 7.1 is fine for an advocacy presentation but would not be suitable for a non-biased appraisal presentation.

Can a portion of the full data set ever be presented in a manner that is not misleading? The answer is "yes," as long as the narrow focus is disclosed explicitly and the purpose of narrowing the margins is disclosed. It may be that the small difference is critical to the analysis and the presentation of the entire margin would obscure the difference. Again, as long as this is disclosed, there is no deception.

Example 3: Color My World

With computer graphics, everyone is now an artist. The use of color can be an effective tool for graphic presentations. It can also be an effective way to literally shade your data and mislead the reader. Figure 7.3 is a great example of this type of presentation.

This graph, produced in 2002, seems to indicate a strong surge in housing prices. Looking at the x-axis, however, all of the strong growth (the darkly shaded area) is situated in the *projected* portion of the data. The historic portion of the chart indicates a much lower rate of annual increase in housing values for this market. Are the projections valid? The answer is unclear, but it is clear that other factors must be considered, not just of the data on the graph. The historic data does not support the increase projected. In addition, the use of color shading should bring out an explicit distinction between the slowly increasing historic data and the faster growing projected data. Let the reader identify this reality. The appraiser may be able to defend the optimistic projection in the model by adding other factors to the analysis.

Example 4: "Trust Me" to the Third Power

One of the more powerful statistical tools presented in this book is the plotting of a trend line over a spread of data points. While this is an excellent way to link points and derive an overall conclusion, the method also presents a perfect opportunity to lead the reader to conclusions that may not be supported by the market or the data. Figure 7.4 is an example of such an application (or misapplication).

Figure 7.3   Average Housing Prices

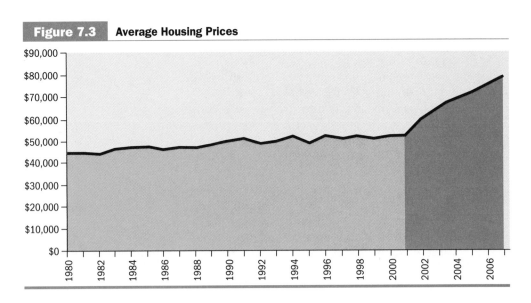

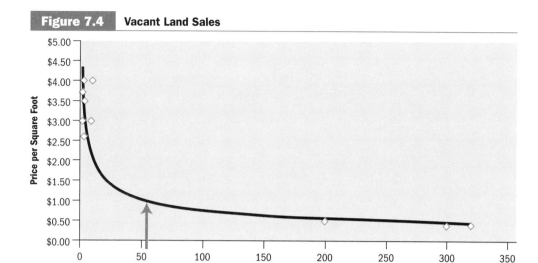

Figure 7.4 Vacant Land Sales

The points represent 10 individual land sales; the orange arrow represents the 50-acre subject site. The trend line appears to provide a good link between data points, and someone reading the trend line would likely conclude a unit value of approximately $1 per square foot for the subject. Upon closer examination, however, several problems appear. First, most appraisers would question the scale of the comparable properties, which range from parcels that are less than one acre to those over 300 acres in size. The subject is a little over 50 acres. Although nicely bracketed by the sales in the graph, this pictorial elegance is offset by appraisal reality. Should a 50-acre parcel be valued using comparable parcels of less than one acre?

Note the scale differences in the graph. The x-axis represents acres, while the unit of comparison shown on the y-axis is sale price per square foot. Are 300-acre parcels sold using the same unit of comparison as one-acre parcels? If larger parcels are sold per acre and smaller parcels are sold per square foot, the appraiser can simply convert one unit into the other, but isn't this an indication that the groups represent different submarkets for land? And what of highest and best use considerations? Is the highest and best use of a one-acre parcel the same or even similar to the highest and best use of a 300-acre parcel?

A final problem concerns the trend line itself. Technically, the line is a quadratic trend line, with a squared term that allows the line to bend as it does. The quadratic equation to create this trend line is called the *functional form* of the line. A rule of thumb for valuation modelers is that the mechanics of any functional form should be market-based. That is, the use of a quadratic formula implies that land purchasers in this market use such a formula in their market transactions. It is much more probable that the relationship is represented by a series of segmented straight lines, like the segmented lines in the case study in Chapter 5 involving scale adjustments.

Most real estate market participants behave in linear terms. There are instances when a more complex form can be used, but it must be thoroughly explained. The authors suspect that the graph in Figure 7.4 really represents two or more land sale market segments conveniently presented as a single entity in this highly speculative graphic. Neither market may be applicable to the subject.

Example 5: The Ballad of the Over-Precise

Appraisers love to round their value conclusions, partly due to uncertainty–valuation is, after all, an opinion of value, not mechanical engineering. Another, perhaps more critical, reason is based on a simple lack of precision. Appraisers should not use any statistical or other valuation technique to impress the reader with an overblown accuracy that is simply not present in the market (or in the appraisal).

Real estate valuation involves human action, which by definition is probabilistic. Such activity cannot be predicted with 100% accuracy. The use of statistical theory recognizes that. We use tables and charts and probability theory to chart the expected course of human action and market behavior. This is never an exact science. The presentation of such accuracy is misleading. Figure 7.5 is an example of an over-precise valuation model.

Although the data points and trend line are nicely arrayed in the chart, both the x- and y-axes are very narrow in scale. Although the graph purports to represent a diminishing marginal unit value as unit sizes increase, it actually supports the conclusion that *no* significant relationship exists. One way to read graphs is to take an example from the data and determine whether it makes appraisal sense. The following statement could be constructed using the data relationship shown in Figure 7.5:

> A significant decline in the marginal sale price per square foot of condominium units is indicated in the graph above. For example, a 1,050-sq.-ft. unit would be expected to sell for $106 per square foot, while a larger 1,200-sq.-ft. unit would likely sell for $104 per square foot.

demic statistician, was impressive from a format perspective but lacked common sense in terms of appraisal content. The model contained many variables, but three in particular caught the authors' attention:

- Number of bedrooms
- Total living area
- Total rooms

All three were in the model, and when the model was run in front of the audience, the valuation coefficients for all three were muddled, as follows:

Variable	Coefficient
Number of bedroom	−$5,016 per bedroom
Total living area	$500 per square foot
Total rooms	$300 per room

None of the three coefficient values makes appraisal sense. The bedroom value is negative, meaning a home with more bedrooms has *less* value. The sale price per square foot would be okay if the property was located in Aspen, Colorado (but it was not). The price was much too high for most housing markets. In addition, the total rooms coefficient was much too small. Adding an additional room in a house should result in a greater increase in value.

What occurred in this analysis is known as *multicollinearity*, a form of confounding that occurs when two or more variables that value the same or a similar valuation factor are included in the model. All three of the above variables are measures of scale, that is, measures of the size of the home. Using all three confounds the regression model and results in offsetting values. When these coefficients are used in the whole model, the value is actually reasonable. The model fails when the coefficients are presented. Models with such coefficients cannot be used in appraisal because the reader is left to trust the model without any way to verify whether it makes sense from a valuation perspective. Once again, the "trust me" problem from traditional appraisal recurs. Figure 7.6 shows a model for confounding variables in a valuation model.

Other forms of confounding occur when there are critical variables missing from a model. For example, suppose an appraiser is valuing a home in a neighborhood with varying degrees of quality of construction. Unfortunately, the appraiser does not have access to this variable and proceeds to appraise a sin-

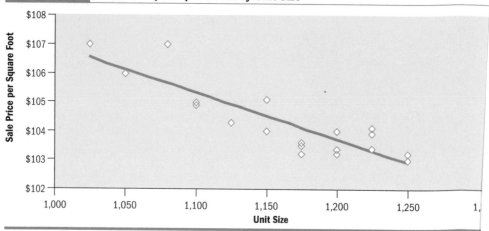

Figure 7.5 Sale Price per Square Foot by Unit Size

The logic of the first sentence is undermined by the absurdity of the second. A $2 diminution in unit value is irrelevant and misleading. People do not transact sales at that level of precision, and neither should the valuation model purporting to represent the market.

The Confounder

Like computer software, real estate valuation analysts have their own viruses, which can be called *confounders*. Confounders are variables that mask the real relationship between two variables. The famous statistical example, outside the realm of real estate, concerns a study of coffee drinkers and lung cancer rates. A medical research study compared the rates of lung cancer between coffee drinkers and non-coffee drinkers. A strong correlation (i.e., a statistically valid relationship) was found, causing consternation in the coffee industry and the coffee-drinking public in general. Upon further analysis, it was found that smoking played a confounding role in the study; coffee drinkers were more apt to smoke cigarettes. Once the study established controls for the effects of smoking, there was no increase in lung cancer rates among coffee drinkers.

In appraisal, the problem generally appears between independent variables in a valuation model. Usually, a good dose of appraisal common sense is sufficient to rid the valuation model of this virus. For example, one of the first presentations of a residential AVM witnessed by the authors involved a model that used thousands of sales. The presentation, by an aca-

Figure 7.6 Confounding Variables in Valuation

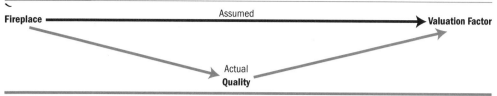

gle-family home using the variables that are available. The following model is presented next:

Valuation Factors (i.e., Coefficients)	Value
Gross living area	$105 per square foot
Number of bathrooms	$3,500 per bathroom
Garage parking	$4,000 per car space
Basement area	$50 per square foot
Finished basement	$20 per square foot
Ranch style	$25,000, if ranch
Air-conditioning	$3,500, if yes
Number of fireplaces	$20,000

All of the valuation factors are reasonable, with the exception of the last variable that indicates $20,000 per fireplace. This value appears to be out of line with the other variables and typical market values, assuming a typical neighborhood. (Upscale homes could conceivably have such expensive fireplaces, but not in a neighborhood with homes valued at $105 per square foot.) What may be happening in the model is that the missing variable, **Quality of Construction**, could be hidden within the **Number of Fireplaces** variable. If upscale homes in this neighborhood have more fireplaces than homes of average quality, then it is possible that the variable **Number of Fireplaces** is actually acting as a proxy variable for **Quality of Construction**.

To solve this problem, the appraiser can perform several data verification checks, which will be covered in the following chapter on modeling applications. Here, the reader is simply forewarned that valuation factors *must* always be checked for validity to ensure that they measure what their name implies.

CHAPTER 8

Modeling Applications

"I know what you're thinkin'. Did he fire six shots or only five? Well, to tell the truth, I kinda forgot myself in all the excitement. But bein' this is a .44 Magnum, the most powerful handgun in the world, and will blow your head clean off, there's only one question you should ask yourself... 'Do I feel lucky?' Well, do ya, punk?"

—Clint Eastwood, *Dirty Harry* (1971)

All of the previous chapters have led up to this point, where modeling is applied to appraisal. The basics of analysis can now be applied to valuation to render any mountain of appraisal data into a manageable amount of real information. Furthermore, that information and the statistical model that generated it are directly applicable to the valuation of real property.

Models are representations of how things work. In real estate, value is often determined through the use of a model. The valuation process taught by the Appraisal Institute is a model. The individual approaches to value are all models. Discounted cash flow spreadsheets are models as well. Even the navigation chart in Figure 8.1 is a model, and Figure 8.2 is a model of the modeling process.

Modeling, particularly regression-based modeling, has been used for many years in the assessment field. It has been used by fee appraisal pioneers as well, in limited applications. Valuation models, how-

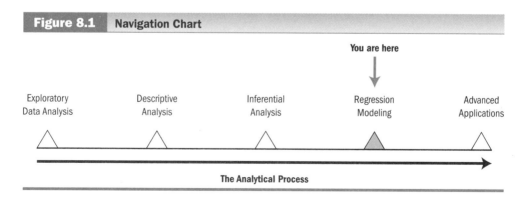

Figure 8.1 Navigation Chart

You are here ↓

| Exploratory Data Analysis | Descriptive Analysis | Inferential Analysis | Regression Modeling | Advanced Applications |

The Analytical Process

· Models are representations of how things work.

· Models may be physical, conceptual, or mathematical.

· Property valuation models seek to explain or predict the market value of properties from real estate data.

Economic Basis of Model Building

Real estate prices—dependent variable

Supply factors

· Building costs

· Interest rates

· Market conditions

Demand factors

· Location

· Condition

· Construction quality

ever, have been used by all appraisers in all aspects of appraisal since the birth of the profession. The old real estate adage that someone can "build it, buy it, or rent it" is a concise description of the market modeling under all three approaches to value. The traditional techniques are valuation models, i.e., models that replicate market factors to determine value based on the specific attributes of the subject property.

Valuation modeling can be as simple as relating sale price to the number of bedrooms in a particular condominium project. It can be as complex as an integrated geographic information system (GIS) surface response model for location. Valuation modeling that employs regression analysis is a powerful tool that all appraisers *must* learn. The authors base this strong opinion on the following observations:

• The need in valuation to use *all* pertinent market data available to the appraiser

• *Limitations* with current manual methods

• The ability to control for *all* factors of valuation

• The ability to test for *significance*

• The ability to test for *accuracy*

• The ability to *convey* results to the reader

Over the last two decades, developments in technology and appraisal have resulted in electronically assisted models that go beyond spreadsheets and words. These are models that rely on underlying economic theory, using mathematical relationships that are analyzed and presented in the scientific language of statistics. Those statistics recognize, expose,

and measure the probabilistic nature of human pref-
erence as well as business decision making.

Basic Steps in Model Building

To develop an effective statistical valuation model,
two important terms must be understood: *model specification* and *model calibration.* The basic steps in
these two integral stages of the modeling process are
outlined in Figure 8.3.

Model Specification

Model specification refers to the process of model
design in which appraisal theory, econometric analysis, and market factors are integrated to select the
proper supply and demand variables. The result is a
formalized valuation model that can be tested against
whole market data.

For most applications, the use of the additive
model is sufficient to value real estate. Other model
forms, such as the multiplicative form and the hybrid
form, are more complex but have a much greater
ability to value a greater range of properties. The
additive model will be used in this book as the primary valuation tool for the sales comparison
approach and the income capitalization approach; it
will also be used to derive the effective age for the
cost approach. The other two model forms are
beyond the scope of this book.

Model specification also includes determining
what specific variables will be used in the model. In the
cost approach, elements such as construction costs and
depreciation can be ascertained from these factors. In
the sales comparison approach, these coefficients
become the adjustment factors that link market sales to
the subject. In the income capitalization approach,
these factors can predict rental rates and capitalization
rates as well as expense and vacancy ratios.

Model specification and calibration are formalized steps that
appraisers already follow when
comparing sales and rents of
comparable properties to the
subject.

Figure 8.3	**Model Specification and Model Calibration**

Specification

- Define the form of the model (additive, multiplicative, hybrid).

then

- Specify which variables should be in the model.

Calibration

- Run the regression model.

then

- Check valuation factors (model coefficients).
- Check accuracy (COV, R-square).

Most relevant market data can be obtained from either third-party vendor sources, such as Comps/CoStar, or from county assessor databases. Pulling data from several sources is an excellent way to add variables; it also provides for good verification of the data.

What determines the specific variables used in the model to value the subject? This depends on the availability of data from the market and the knowledge of the appraiser, who has ultimate control of what goes into the model. If an essential variable is missing from a data set, the model can proceed either with the data missing or with the original data set augmented with data from a separate source. If an essential variable is missing from the model, the appraiser does need to account for a separate step in the analysis.

Model Calibration

Model calibration involves the actual creation of the model. As noted earlier, coefficients are the valuation factors determined by the modeling process. These are equivalent to the adjustment factors or amounts used in traditional appraisal, and they must make sense in the marketplace (see Figure 8.4). For example, a coefficient value of $20,000 for a bathroom may be reasonable for an upscale residential neighborhood, but it is likely excessive for an average neighborhood. It would generally not be used for the valuation of commercial properties.

Model calibration involves running the regression analysis and evaluating the output after each run. The speed and ease of statistical software such as MiniTab and SPSS make this step very easy. The appraiser needs to check both the coefficient values and the modeling accuracy after every run.

Regression Analysis

When both model specification and model calibration have been considered, the appraiser has the opportunity to use a quantitative technique known as *regression analysis*, which identifies the market's response to relevant valuation factors (i.e., variables). Regression analysis permits an equation to be constructed that links each property attribute to a pre-

Figure 8.4 Calibration of the Three Approaches to Value

Cost Approach: calibrated from cost and sales data

Cost data is used to calibrate replacement costs (supply).

Sales data is used to calibrate land values and depreciation (demand).

Sales Comparison Approach: calibrated from sales data

Sales are analyzed statistically en masse rather than individually.

Contributory values of components are estimated directly from market data.

Income Capitalization Approach: calibrated from income and sales data

Income data is used to calibrate economic rents and *NOI*.

Income data and sales data are used to calibrate capitalization rates.

dicted value. When numerous attributes are considered in the regression model, it is known as *multiple regression analysis.*

The additive model *adds* the value of each attribute to determine the value of the dependent variable, which can be sale price, sale price per square foot, potential gross income, or another valuation variable. The additive model is *linear*, meaning that the regression line produced is straight when any of the independent variables (i.e., the valuation factors in the model) are graphed against the dependent variable (sale price, etc.). Of course, a regression model with more than two independent variables could not be graphed this way—graphics are limited to two or three variables because three-dimensional graphs are hard to read.

Statistical Analysis in the Three Approaches to Value

Data analysis is not a separate approach to value; rather, the tools presented in this book can be used throughout the valuation process. (See Figure 8.5.) The cost approach considers the construction costs of a given improvement on a given piece of land, with the land value estimated by some kind of separate analysis (usually sales comparison). Building costs often refer to cost indices provided by vendors such as Marshall and Swift, Dodge, and others. These indices are themselves a form of statistical compilation; that is, they are derived from the typical costs of construction, a model based on measures of central tendency of construction costs. Other factors such as time and location are used to modify the cost index values. Neighborhood ranges, predominant values, vacancy rates, and land uses are forms of descriptive statistics. In many ways appraisers already use statistical analysis in the cost approach as well as in descriptions of market, neighborhood, and economic conditions.

The income capitalization approach is another statistical model of value. Comparable rental properties are organized in an array and then analyzed to select the most competitive properties to determine a market rental rate. The process of selecting, adjusting, and reconciling these arrayed properties to estimate market value can be straightforward or complex. Many commercial appraisers use simple statistical analysis applications in their appraisal reports, from something as fundamental as the determination of an appropriate capitalization rate or gross rent multiplier to techniques as sophisticated as compil-

Figure 8.5   Model Structure for the Three Approaches

Cost Approach Model

Requires estimates of

· Land values

· Reproduction or replacement cost new of improvements

Model structure

value = land value + (reproduction or replacement cost new − depreciation)

Direct Sales Comparison Approach Model

Requires

· Verified sales database

· Contributory value of components

Model structure

value = comparable sale price +/− adjustment to subject

Income Capitalization Approach Model

Requires

· Net operating income

· Capitalization rates for similar use properties

Model structure

value = income / rate

---

ing property and market data to support the use of discounted cash flow analysis.

Appraisers apply modeling principles and statistical analysis directly in the third approach, sales comparison analysis. The variable being measured (i.e., the dependent variable) is usually the market value of the property. Sales comparison simply relates the prices of similar properties to the subject property using either a manual or spreadsheet adjustment mechanism or a valuation model. The valuation model will use multiple regression or some other mathematical process to calculate the appropriate adjustment factors. The sales comparison approach also clearly illustrates the three steps used in statistical analysis; that is, it helps the appraiser select comparable properties (identification), measure differences in property characteristics (measurement), and apply adjustment amounts (interpretation) to arrive at an estimate of value.

Cost Approach

Four elements of the cost approach are typically modeled:

· Replacement costs

· Depreciation factors

· Time/location modification factors

· Market adjustments

> The principles of appraisal valuation modeling are essentially those that have traditionally been used for single-property appraisal. The primary difference is that the former has a greater emphasis on whole market behavior, using tables, ratios, rates, equations, and schedules. Appraisal valuation modeling takes traditional valuation modeling further by using statistical methods to handle large data sets. It is the single-property valuation application under mass appraisal.

Some of these, such as replacement costs, already represent valuation factors, but they may need further market refinements.

Numerous sources for replacement cost data are available for use in cost models. Services such as Marshall & Swift provide data for each major property class, and this data is available for either a unit of comparison such as cost per square foot or segmented costs for various property components.

Depreciation can be extracted from the market, which is somewhat different from the straight-line factors that are normally considered in single-property appraisal. Extracting depreciation from the market through use of regression techniques is straightforward, as will be demonstrated later in this chapter. Extracted depreciation costs can be measured using the age of a given property as an appropriate adjustment factor.

Location and time factors can affect cost factors. While costs throughout a unified market area are generally stable, appraisers should ensure that local variations in costs are monitored to reflect actual costs. Similarly, it is critical to reflect any changes in base costs over time. Any inflationary trend requires an adjustment so that the costs reflect current market costs. Inflationary factors can influence construction costs, and care must be taken to ensure that the most recent costs are reflected in the base replacement cost factors used. Most standardized cost manuals provide adjustment factors for these elements.

While the proper application of each of the previously considered factors tends to minimize the need for any final adjustment factors, an appraiser should consider how cost relates to market value. This can be accomplished by comparing predicted values from a cost approach analysis against sale prices to see how closely the cost model predicts sale prices. This step can be applied in the reconciliation stage of the appraisal.

Direct Sales Comparison Analysis

The sales comparison approach is the model that comes to mind whenever AVMs are mentioned. Indeed, most vendor AVMs are modeled after the direct sales comparison approach because they are typically used to value residential properties and sales comparison is the primary valuation method used by appraisers for that type of property. Direct sale comparison analysis can appear in two places in the appraisal valuation model: to value vacant land as part of the cost approach and to value the overall property as part of the sales comparison approach. Both applications use market-based adjustments to predict the value of the subject.

Adjustment factors have traditionally been applied to comparable sales in the sales comparison approach for single-property appraisal. Traditional adjustments, which are either whole dollar or percentage, quantitative or qualitative, can be expedited through the use of spreadsheets. In an AVM, adjustments are inserted directly into the valuation equation. Further refinements can include the selection of a sample of comparable properties after the valuation equation has been concluded.

Traditionally, sales comparison adjustments have followed an order, e.g., market trend adjustments before physical and location adjustments. Regression modeling allows for simultaneous adjustments for these elements. More importantly, regression modeling can control for the influence for all other factors when determining the adjustment for a particular element. Manual adjustments cannot be made simultaneously or control for other elements. Regression models can handle unlimited data sets and variables as well.

With sufficient sales, regression modeling can predict values for many property types with exceptional accuracy. The equations developed can be used to provide uniform valuations for either a single property or group of properties. Most importantly, the accuracy of the model can be estimated. This last step is not only desirable but probably mandatory. Future standards of practice will likely require it.

Income Capitalization Approach Analysis

There are three components of value that can be derived using modeling in the income capitalization approach:

- The determination of the subject's income potential based on comparable rents
- The determination of vacancy and expense factors
- The determination of direct capitalization rates

All of these can be modeled using comparable income data with the same adjustment procedure applied in the sales comparison approach. They can then be applied in the income pro forma or discounted cash flow analysis, which are both valuation models.

Rental rates from comparable properties can be modeled much like sale properties. Appraisers must determine what property attributes contribute to value and follow the same model specification and calibration steps detailed earlier. The dependent variable here is not sale price, but the potential gross income.

Vacancy and expense rates can also be modeled, based on a comparison of property attributes between the subject and comparable rental properties. The dependent variable in these models is the estimated vacancy or expense rate. If the property is in a market that has varying vacancy rates over time, a time trend analysis similar to a market sales trend analysis can be performed. The projected rate would be the vacancy rate, as opposed to an inflation rate. For markets with triple net leases, appraisers can still model reported management and replacement allowance rates for an expense model that will predict the rate for the subject.

The modeling of direct capitalization rates can use sales data or other property data with reported capitalization rates. The model can then compare property attributes, such as condition, scale, and quality, to predict the subject's capitalization rate.

Case Study

An actual regression model is presented later in the book. This case study will demonstrate how to apply the theory described up to this point. The subject property is an owner-occupied office/warehouse located in an industrial district that has the following property attributes:

Year of construction:	1970
Land area:	2 acres
Zoning:	Industrial
Improved area:	30,000 square feet
Condition:	Average
Construction:	Masonry, average quality, single-tenant
Office finish:	20%
Status:	Owner-occupied
Warehouse section:	20-foot clear span Fixed sprinkler Two overhead doors Two dock-hi doors No truck wells
Fixed equipment:	None
Parking:	50 spaces
Landscaping:	Minimal
Access:	Average for district
Effective date of appraisal:	April 2002

The Sales Comparison Approach

Model Specification. Typically, commercial properties should be modeled using either an additive model or a multiplicative model. Since the multiplicative model is for more advanced users, the additive model will be used in this case study. The important consideration in using this model form is that the sales data must be narrower in range than would be necessary for the multiplicative model. This will guide the exploratory data analysis steps in preparing the data for model calibration.

The following valuation factors were available from the market and were concluded to be relevant for the sales comparison approach:

Dependent Variable	Independent Variables
Sale price	Sale date
	Land area
	Improved area
	Office finish percentage
	Condition (above-average, average, below-average)
	Construction type (metal, masonry)
	Dock-hi doors
	Sprinkler (yes/no)
	Number of stories
	Location (city)
	Year of construction
	Parking space

The next step is to convert any nominal or ordinal data into continuous data for the regression model. Regression models must use continuous data, but there are a few tricks that can easily transform categorical noncontinuous data into continuous data. The major technique is the use of *dummy variables.* These variables take two or more categories of variables and create dummy variables that are coded 0 or 1 for each variable.

For example, the sprinkler category has a "yes" or "no" response, as shown in Table 8.1. This variable is ready for inclusion into the model using the coding 0 = No and 1 = Yes. If the responses had been different, such as Yes = 2 and No = 1, then the values would have had to be recoded as 0, 1.

Table 8.1		Sprinkler Variable Frequency Distribution			
		Frequency	Percent	Valid Percent	Cumulative Percent
Valid	No	270	61.8	61.8	61.8
	Yes	167	38.2	38.2	100.0
	Total	437	100.0	100.0	

The model will treat a binary variable like a continuous variable. If significant, the value of the coefficient represents the added value from the presence of the variable. For example, if metal structures had on the average $100,000 less value than non-metal structures, then any sale property with a code of 1 (meaning that it was a metal structure) would be adjusted downward by $100,000.

Figure 8.6 provides a conceptual view of how a dummy variable adjusts a regression line using two variables. In the example, dummy variables shift the regression line by a fixed amount if the variable is present. If "ranch" and "two-story" were the only types of houses in the data set, then a single dummy variable, **Ranch**, could be created and coded as 1 = Yes and 0 = No. Any property for which the **Ranch** variable had a value of 0 would obviously be a two-story home, the only other option. In the linear regression equation, the coefficient of the **Ranch** variable would equal the difference between the two regression lines, i.e., the dummy variable value shown in the line graph.

If there is more than one category, such as with construction type as shown in Table 8.2, then a series of dummy variables could be created. For this example, a variable called **Metal** could be created, and all metal buildings could be coded 1 and all non-metal buildings 0. Or individual variables could be created for each unique construction type, perhaps combining similar categories such as **Concrete block/stucco** and **Concrete block**. Although in the following model the

Figure 8.6   Regression Line with Two Variables

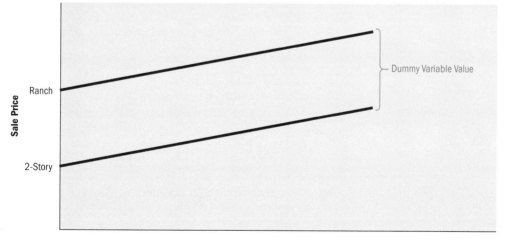

Table 8.2	Construction Type Frequency Distribution			
	Frequency	**Percent**	**Valid Percent**	**Cumulative Percent**
Valid Concrete block/ stucco	6	1.4	1.4	1.4
Concrete block	85	19.7	19.7	21.1
Concrete tilt-up	56	12.8	12.8	33.9
Concrete/steel	5	1.1	1.1	35.0
Frame/wood	5	1.1	1.1	36.2
Masonry	31	7.1	7.1	43.2
Metal	65	14.9	14.9	58.1
Mixed construction	41	9.4	9.4	67.5
Not available	7	1.6	1.6	69.1
Poured concrete	11	2.5	2.5	71.6
Precast concrete	37	8.5	8.5	80.1
Steel frame	2	0.5	0.5	80.5
Structural brick	85	19.5	19.5	100.0
Total	437	100.0	100.0	

former option, creating the dummy variable **Metal**, was chosen, this other coding scheme would have also worked. As a statistical rule of thumb, the minimum number of occurrences in a category is six.

The sale file totals 437 sales and includes sales between January 1998 and March 2002. The first step in the analysis is EDA (i.e., exploratory data analysis) of the data to determine outliers and other problems that may be present. Another term often applied is *data reduction* because the number of sales is often significantly reduced at this stage. In addition, since the additive model is being used, the analysis needs to be narrowly focused on the subject attributes. This will further reduce the total number of sales used in the model. Some of the data reduction already occurred in the exploratory data analysis conducted in Chapter 3.

The first step is to examine the sale price distribution with the valuation factor that most appraisers would reasonably expect to be the most important, **Total Improved Area**. In a comparison of two continuous (ratio) variables, a scatter plot such as Figure 8.7 can provide a snapshot of any outliers.

The first conclusion is that there appears to be a wide spread of sales in terms of improved area. Running only the sales of less than 60,000 square feet and greater than 10,000 square feet results in the histogram in Figure 8.8. At this point the sales data has already been reduced dramatically, with the number of sales in the data set reduced to 170.

Note that the process of establishing a systematic reduction in the data can be conveyed to the reader of the appraisal.

Figure 8.7   **Total Improved Area Scatter Plot**

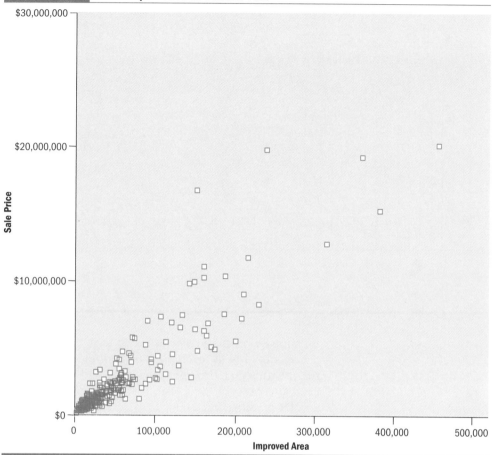

Can you ever use the dependent variable to reduce the scope of data? The answer is yes, but it must be used with caution. Obvious outlier sale prices can be safely excluded, but too much paring down using the sale price (or the dependent variable) can appear to be manipulating the sales analysis. Paring down the data set based on known valuation factors that can be compared to the subject is much more defensible. Remember that at this stage the value of the subject property is not known, so how can reducing the range of sale prices be supported with market evidence?

The next step is to examine other important variables, such as **Location, Age** (based on year of construction), **Condition, Land Area, Office Finish,** and **Construction** (i.e., metal or non-metal). This determination is based on appraisal judgment and can be modified if other variables are ultimately found to be more significant. The reason for using

Spurious relationships occur when two variables appear to be related but in fact are not. For example, a model could be developed between the growth of hair on your head with job creation in Cleveland, Ohio, as both increase over time. While a statistical justification could be developed, common sense would reject it outright.

Figure 8.8 Total Improved Area Histogram

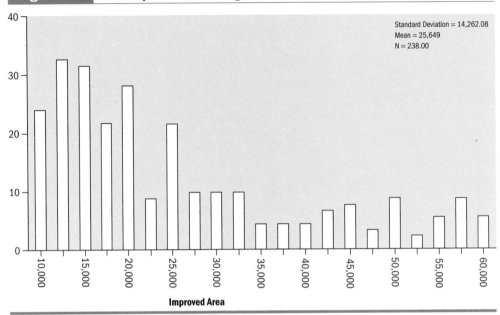

Standard Deviation = 14,262.08
Mean = 25,649
N = 238.00

Improved Area

the most significant variables is that the modeling process begins at this point. By reducing and focusing the analysis, the appraiser can (and must) play a critical role from the outset of the modeling process.

The following series of tables and graphs (Figures 8.9 and 8.10 and Tables 8.3, 8.4, and 8.5) were used to examine for any outliers and problem values for the independent variables. The continuous variables were examined using histograms, while the nominal- and ordinal-level data were analyzed using frequency tables. Since the market trend data is represented by two variables, **Sale Month** and **Sale Year**, a crosstab table was used to determine the distribution for the variable **Sale Period**.

The descriptive statistical tools illustrated in the figures and tables provide a good overview of the sales data set. Given the scope of analysis, properties with the following attributes were deemed appropriate for the analysis:

- Located in Denver only
- Less than 60 years old
- In average condition
- Land area less than 6 acres
- Office finish of less than 40%

The sale period of four years was also judged to be sufficient. All of these constraints were based on the data and appraisal considerations. Fifty sales remain,

Figure 8.9 Age and Land Area Histograms

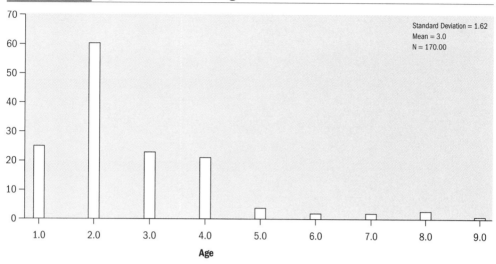

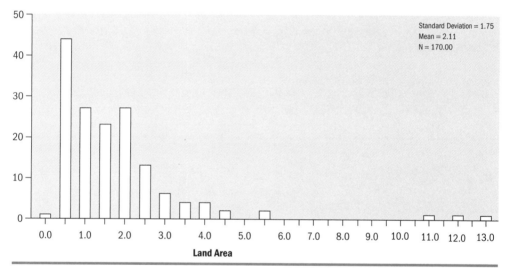

still more than sufficient to model and certainly much greater than the number typically used in traditional fee appraisal.

As a final check, another scatter plot of **Sale Price** against **Improved Area** was run (Figure 8.11). The oval shape of the data points is typically what analysts look for in additive models. The ranges of the dependent variable, **Sale Price,** and the independent variable, **Improved Area,** are both reasonable. Also, **Improved Area** clearly brackets the subject, which has 30,000 square feet.

Now the identification step of the analysis is complete. The data has been analyzed and reduced from over 400 sales to 50 sales by identifying the critical variables and ranges of values based on the valuation

Table 8.3   Month and Year Crosstabulation

Count		1998	1999	2000	2001	2002	Total
				Year			
Month	1	0	3	3	3	5	14
	2	0	3	3	4	2	12
	3	0	5	5	2	6	18
	4	2	4	2	2	1	11
	5	1	3	5	1	0	10
	6	6	4	3	1	0	14
	7	3	7	2	4	0	16
	8	0	7	3	2	0	12
	9	4	5	6	3	0	18
	10	1	2	4	6	0	13
	11	1	1	3	4	0	9
	12	7	8	6	2	0	23
Total		25	52	45	34	14	170

Table 8.4   Recoded Building Condition

		Frequency	Percent	Valid Percent	Cumulative Percent
Valid	Above-average condition	28	16.5	16.5	16.5
	Average condition	132	77.6	77.6	94.1
	Below-average condition	10	5.9	5.9	100.0
	Total	170	100.0	100.0	

Table 8.5   Property City

		Frequency	Percent	Valid Percent	Cumulative Percent
Valid	Arvada	7	4.1	4.1	4.1
	Aurora	11	6.5	6.5	10.6
	Brighton	3	1.8	1.8	12.4
	Broomfield	3	1.8	1.8	14.1
	Commerce City	8	4.7	4.7	18.8
	Denver	82	48.2	48.2	67.1
	Englewood	27	15.9	15.9	82.9
	Golden	4	2.4	2.4	85.3
	Henderson	1	0.6	0.6	85.9
	Lakewood	5	2.9	2.9	88.8
	Littleton	6	3.5	3.5	92.4
	Longmont	4	2.4	2.4	94.7
	Louisville	2	1.2	1.2	95.9
	Northglenn	1	0.6	0.6	96.5
	Thornton	1	0.6	0.6	97.1
	Wheat Ridge	5	2.9	2.9	100.0
	Total	170	100.0	100.0	

Figure 8.10
Office Finish and Construction Type Histograms

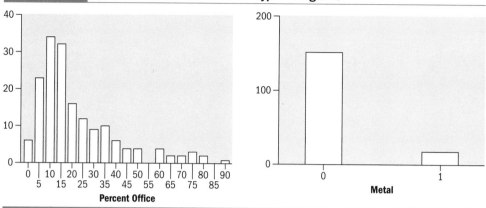

Percent Office

Metal

Figure 8.11
Improved Area Scatter Plot

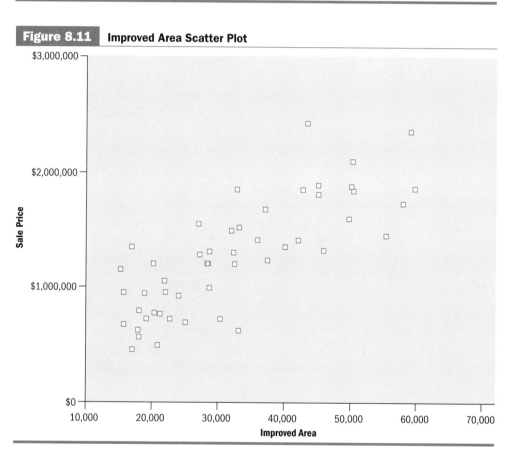

Improved Area

factors (i.e., the independent variables). In addition, the market has been systematically scanned for appropriate data, and the subject's position within the overall market has been established. As part of this process, nominal and ordinal variables were recoded into dummy variables so they could be included in the model.

The next step is to actually run the regression model in SPSS. In the analytical process, this is the measurement step. It also serves as the calibration step in the modeling process because the regression model will run all of the variables against the sale prices of the 50 sale properties to determine the probable market value of the subject.

Model Calibration. Both SPSS and MiniTab provide several options in additive regression models. All of these methods concern how variables are entered into the model. The enter method runs the model with all of the variables, whether they are significant or not. The stepwise method enters variables one by one, based on their relative significance. The most significant variables are entered first. Because of the relationship between the independent variables, some variables can drop out throughout this process.

The stepwise process stops when the last significant variable is entered. What determines the significance? The relative significance is calculated for each variable. The model allows variables to enter based on their p value, which is the significance statistic that measures the probability that the variable's association to sale price is due to random chance. It is interpreted like the significance measures first encountered in the t-tests. The regression run output in this chapter is based on the stepwise method.

Although the initial model appeared promising, the first runs of the regression model yielded wide variation (over 20% COV) and R-square values that were disappointing. The appraisers noted in the initial runs that three sales of smaller properties were not being modeled effectively. Given that none of these sales were comparable to the subject, the appraisers removed these three properties from further modeling, reducing the data set to 47 sales. This resulted in a much better model.

The output from SPSS shown in Table 8.6 was the first run using the 47 sales. This table provides the descriptive overview of the dependent and independent variables in the model. **Sale Price** is self-explanatory. **Land Area** is the total acreage for each sale property. The **Improved Area** variable was reported

In addition to stepwise regression, other types of regression models include

- Enter, where all independent variables are entered in a single step
- Forward, where variables are entered in a single block
- Backward, where variables are entered in a single block, then removed one at a time based on preset criteria
- Remove, which removes variables in a single block

Typically, appraisers will use either enter or stepwise options when building valuation models.

Table 8.6	Descriptive Statistics		
	Mean	Standard Deviation	N
Sale Price	$1,304,621.66	$477,928.041	47
Land Area	1.6955	0.92072	47
Improved Area	32,654.91	13,197.969	47
Metal	0.0638	0.24709	47
Offper	15.91	10.178	47
Parksp	48.04	40.339	47
Saleper	22.9362	13.94150	47
Age1	37.3191	17.06013	47
Dockhi	4.06	4.834	47
Sprinkl	0.70	0.462	47
Truss	17.70	3.605	47

in gross square feet. The variable **Metal** is a dummy variable, with 0 = non-metal structure and 1 = metal structure. The variable **Offper** is the percentage of office finish reported for each property. **Parksp** is the number of on-site parking spaces. **Saleper** is the sales period, based on the 46 months prior to the effective date of the appraisal; it was coded in reverse, with the first month coded 46 and the last month, April 2002 (the effective date of the appraisal), coded 0. **Age1** is self-explanatory. **Dockhi** denotes the number of dock-hi doors for each property. **Sprinkl** is a binary variable that was already coded 0 for no sprinkler system and 1 for the presence of a fixed sprinkler system. Finally, the variable **Truss** is the clearspan height in the warehouse section of each property.

Based on the variables chosen for the model, the output shown in Table 8.7 was created. The stepwise model cycled seven times, resulting in the last line of the output box. The third, shaded column provides the indication of the overall explanatory power of the model. The 0.825 ratio translates into the conclusion that approximately 82.5% of the variation between sale price and the set of independent variables is explained by the model. Another good indication is derived from the next column, showing the standard error of the estimate. If you divide this by the average sale price, the resulting percentage represents an approximation of the COV. With a COV of -15.3%(+/-), this is a good overall model in terms of average error and fit for a commercial property.

The next step involves the interpretation of the valuation factors calibrated by the model, represented in Table 8.8 by the coefficients in the shaded box. The actual output included other rows that referenced the previous stepwise cycles. The last cycle, Model 7, is shown in Table 8.8. Although promising, several coefficient values cause concern. Both of the last two values are negative, which implies that adding dock-hi doors or a sprinkler system causes a loss in value. This, of course, goes against appraisal common sense. In this case, the analysts believed that both variables were reflecting the relatively lower value of the warehouse space (relative to the office finish space) in some manner. Given that the other variables were indicating reasonable values, the analysts decided to recalibrate the model, running it without either the **Dockhi** or **Sprinkl** vari-

Table 8.7	Model Summary (h)				
Model	R	R-Square	Adjusted R-Square	Standard Error of the Estimate
1	.803(a)	.645	.638	$287,705.018
2	.842(b)	.709	.696	$263,558.438
3	.886(c)	.785	.770	$228,959.937
4	.898(d)	.806	.788	$220,275.837
5	.908(e)	.825	.803	$211,954.410
6	.916(f)	.839	.815	$205,361.095
7	.923(g)	.851	.825	$200,033.784

a. Predictors: (Constant), Improved Area

b. Predictors: (Constant), Improved Area, Saleper

c. Predictors: (Constant), Improved Area, Saleper, Parksp

d. Predictors: (Constant), Improved Area, Saleper, Parksp, Offper

e. Predictors: (Constant), Improved Area, Saleper, Parksp, Offper, Truss

f. Predictors: (Constant), Improved Area, Saleper, Parksp, Offper, Truss, Dockhi

g. Predictors: (Constant), Improved Area, Saleper, Parksp, Offper, Truss, Dockhi, Sprinkl

h. Dependent Variable: Sale Price

Table 8.8	Coefficients (a)				
Model	Unstandardized Coefficients		Standardized Coefficients	T	Sig.
	B	Standard Error	Beta		
7 (Constant)	37444.376	179023.237		.209	.835
Improved Area	28.743	2.589	.794	11.102	.000
Saleper	-9701.023	2193.393	-.283	-4.423	.000
Parksp	2854.535	888.405	.241	3.213	.003
Offper	6971.307	3045.638	.148	2.289	.028
Truss	25569.115	9691.031	.193	2.638	.012
Dockhi	-15413.354	6972.405	-.156	-2.211	.033
Sprinkl	-123911.413	69717.418	-.120	-1.777	.083

a. Dependent Variable: Sale Price

ables. The output in Table 8.9 describes the result of this run.

As suspected, the overall fit and the standard error of the new model are slightly inferior. The implied COV was derived by dividing the standard error of $211,954 by the mean sale price, or $1,304,622. This results in a COV of 16.2%. In addition, the R-square was 0.803, or 80.3%. While both evaluation statistics are slightly inferior to the previous model, they are still well within established thresholds for commercial modeling. The benefit of this model is that the coefficients for each of the variables now have real meaning and applicability to evaluations.

The real indication of the model's applicability to the subject is Table 8.10, which shows the coefficient values for all model cycles from this stepwise run. Note that with the exclusion of the variables **Dockhi** and **Sprinkl,** there were only five stepwise cycles.

The shaded area highlights the final stepwise model and coefficient values (i.e., valuation factors). All of the coefficients appear reasonable in terms of these values.

Improved area	=	$26.29 per square foot
Market trend	=	-$9,459 per month
Parking space	=	$2,665 per space
Office finish	=	$8,318 per 1% office finish
Truss height	=	$20,905 per foot

Generally, the constant value is also part of the valuation equation. In this case, the constant was not

Table 8.9	Model Summary (f)			
Model	R	R-Square	Adjusted R-Square	Standard Error of the Estimate
1	.803(a)	.645	.638	$287,705.018
2	.842(b)	.709	.696	$263,558.438
3	.886(c)	.785	.770	$228,959.937
4	.898(d)	.806	.788	$220,275.837
5	.908(e)	.825	.803	$211,954.410

a. Predictors: (Constant), Improved Area

b. Predictors: (Constant), Improved Area, Saleper

c. Predictors: (Constant), Improved Area, Saleper, Parksp

d. Predictors: (Constant), Improved Area, Saleper, Parksp, Offper

e. Predictors: (Constant), Improved Area, Saleper, Parksp, Offper, Truss

f. Dependent Variable: Sale Price

Table 8.10	Coefficients (a)					
Model		**Unstandardized Coefficients**		**Standardized Coefficients**	**T**	**Sig.**
		B	**Standard Error**	**Beta**		
1	(Constant)	354564.313	113035.624		3.137	.003
	Improved Area	29.094	3.214	.803	9.052	.000
2	(Constant)	507162.503	114639.066		4.424	.000
	Improved Area	30.573	2.983	.844	10.250	.000
	Saleper	-8759.382	2823.654	-.256	-3.102	.003
3	(Constant)	465655.702	100153.521		4.649	.000
	Improved Area	27.733	2.691	.766	10.306	.000
	Saleper	-10147.772	2478.524	-.296	-4.094	.000
	Parksp	3457.343	883.813	.292	3.912	.000
4	(Constant)	364563.525	107596.724		3.388	.002
	Improved Area	27.469	2.592	.759	10.598	.000
	Saleper	-9874.021	2388.040	-.288	-4.135	.000
	Parksp	3369.844	851.301	.284	3.958	.000
	Offper	6763.160	3203.428	.144	2.111	.041
5	(Constant)	32640.194	189664.917		.172	.864
	Improved Area	26.289	2.557	.726	10.280	.000
	Saleper	-9459.454	2306.382	-.276	-4.101	.000
	Parksp	2664.886	885.950	.225	3.008	.004
	Offper	8318.174	3171.046	.177	2.623	.012
	Truss	20905.158	10008.752	.158	2.089	.043

a. Dependent Variable: Sale Price

significant and will therefore not be part of the final valuation equation for the subject. Based on the attributes of the subject, the following value was concluded:

Constant	(not significant)	=	$0
Improved area	$26.29 × 30,000	=	$788,700
Market trend	$9,459 × 0	=	$0
Parking space	$2,665 × 50	=	$133,250
Office finish	$8,318 × 20	=	$166,360
Truss height	$20,905 × 20	=	$418,100
Total			**$1,506,410**

Note that because the subject property is being valued when the value of the variable **Saleper** is 0 (i.e., the effective date of the appraisal), the sale adjustment is zero.

The subject property's value of $1,506,410 results in a rate of $50.21 per square foot. To verify the accuracy of the model, the appraisers evaluated the model's accuracy using a sales ratio analysis. This type of evaluation process is performed in conjunction with the two evaluation statistics (COV and R-square) already mentioned. A sales ratio is simply the estimated value of each sale divided by the sale price:

sales ratio = predicted value/sale price

Accuracy is determined by both the average sales ratio of all 47 sales as well as the spread of the individual ratios around the mean ratio.

Once the sales ratio is calculated, the appraiser can check it against the major variables in the model. The goal is to have the ratio as close to 1.0 as possible and to avoid having any extreme outliers or patterns in the errors. An error pattern occurs when there is a pattern in the sales ratios or if there are extreme ratios clustered at either end of the variable range. If present, it may be best to exclude sales at those extremes and rerun the model. The graphs in Figure 8.12 are examples using the sales ratio to evaluate the model.

Chart A shows a histogram of the sales ratios for the 47 sales. The ratios cluster around 1.0, although there are several that represent outliers. Chart B is a scatter plot of the sales ratios by improved area. Of particular interest is the middle range of improved area, where the subject would be. There are several sales with extreme ratio values that could require field inspections to determine if there are any factors not accounted for in the model. Chart C represents a box and whisker plot comparison of metal and non-metal buildings. Only three of the 47 sale properties were metal structures; their median sales ratio and distribution appear to mimic the non-metal building sales. Another check is presented in Chart D, which is a scatter plot of the sales ratios by sale price. Comparing the sales ratio to the sale price (or whatever is the dependent variable) allows the appraiser to check for what is termed the *price-related differential* (PRD).

In mass appraisal models, there can be a tendency to have the ratios follow a pattern based on the sale price. A *regressive* model has the ratios lie above 1.0 for lower-priced properties and below 1.0 for higher-priced properties, meaning the model tends to overvalue properties less than the mean sale price and undervalue properties greater than the mean. A *progressive* model does just the opposite. Its ratios tend to be less than 1.0 for properties below the mean and greater than 1.0 for properties greater than the mean; thus it undervalues lower-priced properties

price-related differential (PRD). The mean divided by the weighted mean. The statistic has a slight upward bias. Price-related differentials above 1.03 tend to indicate assessment regressivity (i.e., higher-priced properties being assessed lower than lower-priced properties in relation to market value); price-related differentials below 0.98 tend to indicate assessment progressivity (i.e., higher-priced properties being assessed proportionally higher than lower-priced properties).

Figure 8.12 Sales Ratio Graphics

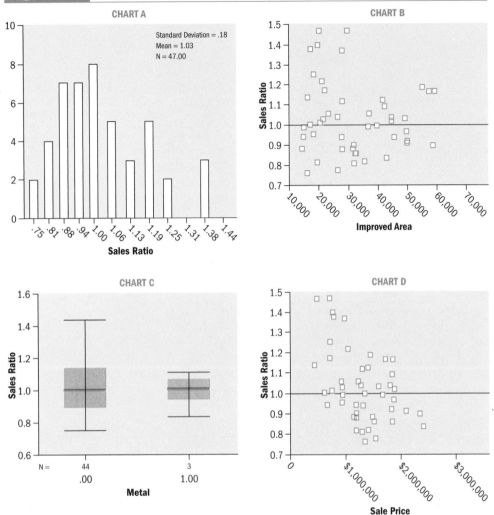

AVM models used by the private sector have to contend with the price-related differential because they also value all properties (just one at a time).

and overvalues higher-priced properties. In assessment, this is a critical determination because all properties must be valued and assessors cannot use biased models that treat properties unequally.

For single-property appraisal, the price-related differential can be a concern if the subject property's value conclusion strays too far from the mean sale price. Chart D indicates that the model is somewhat regressive, given that the ratios appear to lie consistently above 1.0 for lower-priced properties and below 1.0 for higher-priced properties. Since the subject's valuation conclusion lies in the center of the data, the issue of bias is less important.

As part of SPSS output, output ratios can be computed with corresponding COVs, CODs, and PRDs.

Table 8.11	Ratio Statistics for Unstandardized Predicted Value/Sale Price	
Mean		1.030
Median		.999
Minimum		.760
Maximum		1.465
Price-related differential		1.030
Coefficient of dispersion		.137
Coefficient of variation (mean-centered)		17.5%

The ratio output for this model, which is shown in Table 8.11, indicates that the mean and median sales ratios are very close to 1.0. The minimum sales ratio was 0.76 and the maximum was 1.465. The PRD was 1.03, confirming the observation that the model is slightly regressive. The COD is a strong 13.7%, while the COV, more sensitive to outlier ratios, comes in a little higher at 17.5%. Based on the output in Table 8.11, the analysts determined that the model was sound from both an appraisal and a statistical standpoint.

A note about the dependent variable: Analysts often ask whether the sale price or the sale price per square foot should be used as the dependent variable. A COV analysis was performed on the 47-sale data set, but the COV for sale price (at 34%) was not significantly different than the COV for sale price per square foot (at 28%). The final decision to use the sale price rather than the sale price per square foot was based on the model outcomes from both dependent variables. The outcome statistics for the former were superior to the latter.

The Income Capitalization Approach
The next step of the valuation analysis involves use of regression modeling to determine potential gross income (*PGI*) and direct capitalization rates for the income capitalization approach.

Model Specification. To determine the probable income potential for the subject, the analysts returned to the larger industrial data set of more than 400 sales in search of rental data. This data could be augmented by rental data from other sources, or a completely different data set based on industrial rental properties in this market could be used. Out of a total of 437 sales, 57 properties reported rental income. The histogram in Figure 8.13 describes this rental data. The rents range from $2 per square foot to $12 per square foot.

Figure 8.13 Rental Data Histogram

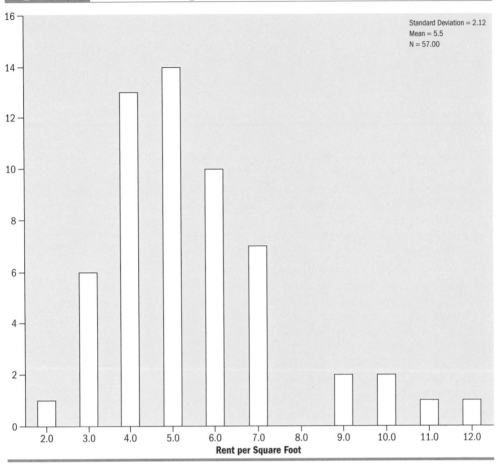

The first step in this model involved the same EDA steps taken in the industrial sales model. (These steps will not be repeated here because they are identical to those presented in the sales comparison approach.) Properties with more than 40% office finish and those over 50 years old were excluded. The reduction was based on the appraisers' judgment and market knowledge. This reduced the rental properties to 37. These rental properties were then modeled, based on the valuation factors shown in Table 8.12. The first shaded variable is the dependent variable, rent per square foot (**Rentsf**). The others are the independent variables that will predict the expected rental rate per square foot.

Model Calibration. The 37 sales were entered into a stepwise regression model, with the results shown in Table 8.13. Although not as tightly fitting as the sales analysis, the results were acceptable. The stepwise process

Having 57 of 437 sale properties report rental data may tell the appraiser about the nature of this industrial market. For example, if this is indicative of all industrial properties in this market, then it provides market evidence of the predominance of owner-user properties (i.e., fee simple ownership) over investor properties (i.e., leased fee ownership). If it does not represent the industrial population, then it still tells the appraiser about current sales activity and market dynamics.

Table 8.12	Descriptive Statistics		
	Mean	**Standard Deviation**	**N**
Rentsf	$4.9465	$1.16466	37
Improved Area	56069.03	56045.680	37
Land Area	3.1817	3.15461	37
Parksp	110.49	134.912	37
Offper	19.73	15.227	37
Metal	.0811	.27672	37
Saleper	22.1622	14.56501	37
Age1	25.4324	11.44683	37

Table 8.13	Model Summary (e)			
Model	**R**	**R-Square**	**Adjusted R-Square**	**Standard Error of the Estimate**
1	.545(a)	.297	.277	$0.99032
2	.782(b)	.611	.588	$0.74728
3	.816(c)	.667	.636	$0.70245
4	.832(d)	.693	.654	$0.68492

a. Predictors: (Constant), Age1

b. Predictors: (Constant), Age1, Offper

c. Predictors: (Constant), Age1, Offper, Improved Area

d. Predictors: (Constant), Age1, Offper, Improved Area, Land Area

e. Dependent Variable: Rentsf

went through four cycles, with the last model shaded. Note that since the dependent variable, **Rentsf**, is a rate, the standard error of $0.68492 is also expressed as a rate. Comparing this error rate to the average rental rate (from Table 8.12) results in a preliminary COV estimate of 13.8% (COV = $0.68/$4.95 = 0.138).

Although the R-square (0.654) in this model is less than in the sales comparison model (0.803), the COV for this model (13.8%) is actually lower than for the other (16.2%). This may appear to be contradictory, but in fact it demonstrates why the COV is a preferable statistic to the R-square for evaluating AVMs. The R-square measures *relative* variation in a model. If the actual ranges of variation for both the dependent variable and independent variables are narrow, then the R-square may become an unreliable statistic. This is explored further in Chapter 10, which covers evaluation of AVMs in detail. For now, it is sufficient to note that for single-property appraisal the COV is *the* evaluation statistic of choice.

As with the direct sales model, the final check uses the Ratio Analysis function in SPSS to measure the model's fit, as shown in Table 8.14. Both the mean and median rent ratios are very close to 1.0.

Likewise, the PRD is also close to 1.0. The COD at 0.108 and COV at 13.5% also indicate the tight range of variation around 1.0.

This run of the stepwise model resulted in the coefficients shown in Table 8.15. As noted earlier, the dependent variable is a rate; all of the coefficient values are also presented as rates. Unlike the direct sale analysis, the constant for the income model is significant and will be included in the rental rate equation. All of the coefficient values make appraisal sense.

Since the dependent variable is stated as a rate per square foot, the negative value of the **Improved Area** variable is evidence of a decline in marginal rental rate as a property grows. The small magnitude of the **Improved Area** coefficient is offset by the larger scale of these properties. The following equation determines the probable rental income potential for the subject, based on the market-derived coefficient values and the subject property's attributes:

$$PGI = \$6.09 - \$0.067\,(30) + \$0.04\,(20) - \$0.0000185\,(30,000) + \$0.247\,(2)$$
$$= \$6.09 - \$2.01 + \$0.80 - \$0.56 + \$0.49$$
$$= \$4.81 \text{ per square foot}$$

Multiplying by the subject's 30,000 square feet results in a potential gross income of $144,300. This total can then be used in the pro forma analysis. If the subject

Table 8.14	Ratio Statistics for Unstandardized Predicted Value/Rentsf	
Mean		1.016
Median		1.002
Minimum		.779
Maximum		1.281
Price-related differential		1.016
Coefficient of dispersion		.108
Coefficient of variation (median-centered)		13.5%

Table 8.15	Coefficients (a)					
Model		Unstandardized Coefficients		Standardized Coefficients	T	Sig.
		B	Standard Error	Beta		
4	(Constant)	6.094	.372		16.362	.000
	Age1	-.067	.011	-.654	-6.152	.000
	Offper	.040	.008	.528	4.953	.000
	Improved Area	-.0000185	.000	-.890	-2.226	.033
	Land Area	.247	.150	-.669	1.646	.109

a. Dependent Variable: Rentsf

had been leased instead of owner-occupied, a further check would have been to compare the actual rents with the result from the model.

The next modeling step concerns the estimation of the direct capitalization rate for the subject. Reported direct capitalization rates from the same rental data set were used. The histogram shown in Figure 8.14 illustrates the distribution of reported direct capitalization rates.

By replacing the dependent variable, **Rentsf,** with the reported direct capitalization rate, **Dircap**, the model can be calibrated to predict the probable direct capitalization rate for the subject. The appraisers used only the age, sale period, and building construction variables for this model. The output from the model shown in Figure 8.15 and Tables 8.16, 8.17, 8.18, and 8.19 indicates the overall fit and the coefficient values.

A review of the output indicates that this statistical model has strong predictive power. The COV was

Figure 8.14 Capitalization Rate Histogram

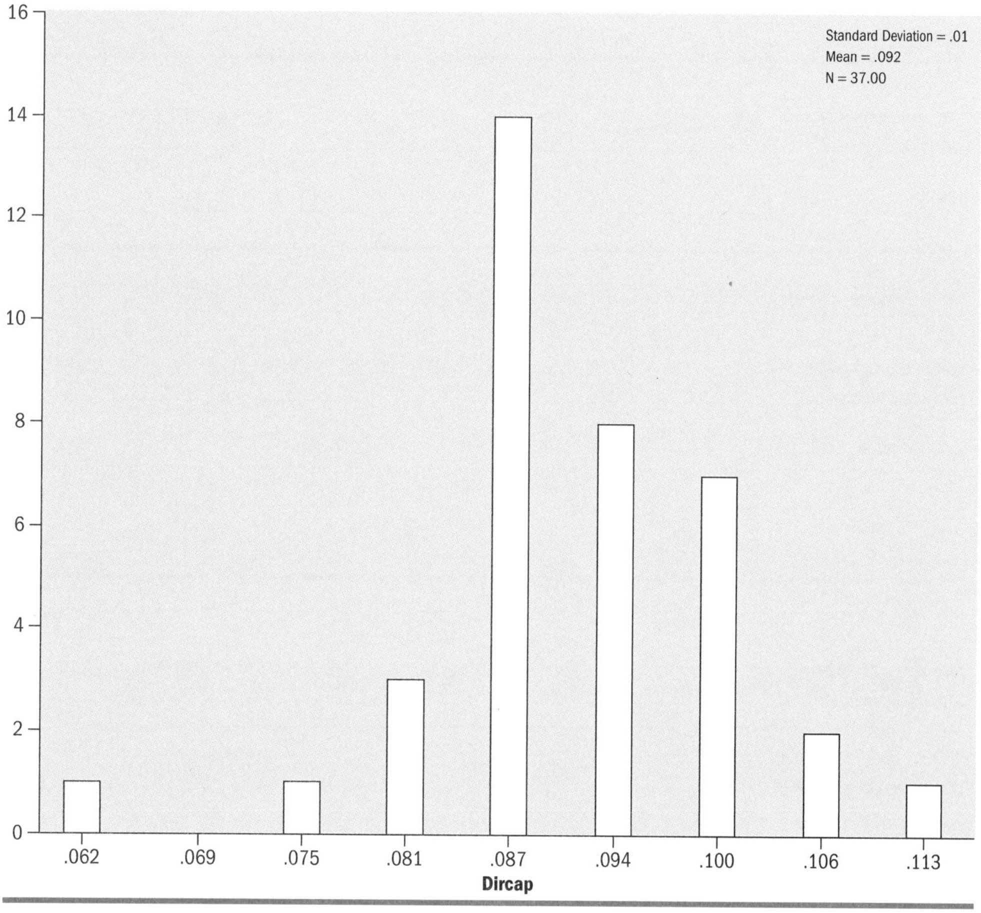

Standard Deviation = .01
Mean = .092
N = 37.00

Figure 8.15   **Age and Capitalization Rate Analysis**

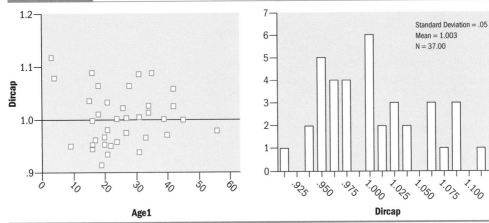

Table 8.16   Descriptive Statistics

	Mean	Standard Deviation	N
Dircap	.09192	.009121	37
Age1	25.4324	11.44683	37
Saleper	22.1622	14.56501	37
Metal	.0811	.27672	37

Table 8.17   Model Summary (b)

Model	R	R-Square	Adjusted R-Square	Standard Error of the Estimate
1	.827(a)	.684	.675	.005197

a. Predictors: (Constant), Age1

b. Dependent Variable: Dircap

Table 8.18   Coefficients (a)

Model	Unstandardized Coefficients		Standardized Coefficients	T	Sig.
	B	Standard Error	Beta		
1 (Constant)	.075	.002		35.695	.000
Age1	.00066	.000	.827	8.711	.000

a. Dependent Variable: Dircap

Table 8.19   Ratio Statistics for Unstandardized Predicted Value/Dircap

Mean	1.004
Median	.996
Price-related differential	1.004
Coefficient of dispersion	.049
Coefficient of variation (median-centered)	6.1%

Figure 8.16 Capitalization Rate Scatter Plot

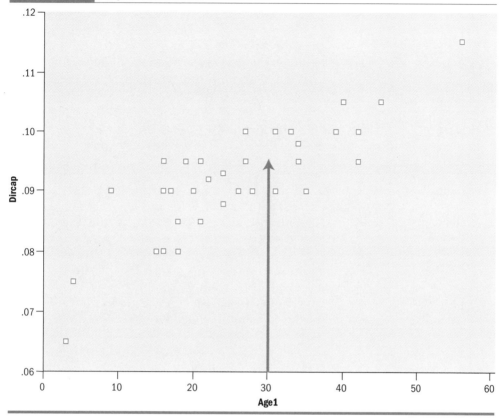

6.1% and the COD was 0.049. All the other indications were much tighter than either of the other two
models. The direct capitalization rate for the subject
is derived as follows:

$$\text{Dircap} = 0.075 + 0.00066 \ (\text{Age})$$
$$= 0.081 + 0.00066 \ (30)$$
$$= 0.075 + 0.02$$
$$= 0.095$$

As a final check, the scatter plot comparing actual direct capitalization rates against the age of each
comparable property, with the subject superim-
posed, was examined (Figure 8.16). The estimated
direct capitalization rate for the subject is clearly
supported by the arrayed data.

Armed with both the potential gross income for
the subject and the direct capitalization rate estimate,
the appraisers can now plug in similar market-
derived estimates for vacancy and expenses. For
example, a model could be derived that predicts the
expense ratio for the subject. A similar model can be

derived to estimate vacancy rates, or a trend analysis could be used that is similar to the market trend analysis for this factor.

The Cost Approach

In the cost approach, AVM applications can be useful tools for determining land value and depreciation. Although there are several methods of estimating the value of the land component, the preferred method is the sales comparison approach using vacant land sales. This type of valuation analysis can use the same type of modeling methodology demonstrated in the direct sales comparison example in this chapter.

A second area in which modeling can enhance the cost approach analysis is the estimation of depreciation based on market sales data. Although chronological age is easily determined by subtracting the year of construction from the effective date of the appraisal, this does not determine the effective age of the subject. In addition, market-based depreciation data is often obscured by other factors of value, leaving the determination of market-derived depreciation to paired sales analysis.

Fortunately, an appraisal valuation model using regression can transform the chronological age variable into an excellent measurement of market depreciation. Although similar to the sales comparison application of the valuation model presented previously, this modeling method focuses on effective age adjustments by limiting the sales database to very similar properties. To calculate effective age, the land component would first need to be removed from the total sale price.

Model Specification. By selecting comparable properties overall, the need to include valuation factors for other property attributes can be eliminated from the analysis. The only independent variable in the model should be chronological age. Again, the sale price excludes the land component because land itself does not depreciate.

Any variable associated with the condition of the property should be excluded. The variable **Condition** itself should be excluded because the goal is to use the **Age** variable to test for depreciation. Leaving a variable like **Condition** in the model would cause problems because the goal of the model is to determine the condition by determining depreciation. (This would be similar to using a sale price-related independent variable in the model while at the same time predicting the sale price.) Since all of the other valuation factors related to improvements are being excluded, the model itself will not yield impressive accuracy. The goal, however, is to isolate the effects of deprecation as measured by age.

Another important specification consideration is the form of the model. As noted previously, the scope of this book precludes the full presentation of any regression modeling more complex than the linear form, but the variation on the linear form presented will include a squared term for **Age**. Appraisal theory and experience suggest that deprecation in the real world may not be linear (i.e., straight-line), so the search for market depreciation should not be limited to the linear form. The diagrams in Figure 8.17 illustrate this point.

The graph on the left shows the basic linear model between the dependent variable (**Sale Price per Square Foot**) and one independent variable (**Age**). The relationship between **Sale Price per Square Foot** and **Age** is linear. The rate of change in **Sale Price per Square Foot** is constant over all **Age** values, hence the straight line. The graph on the right illustrates a different relationship. The line bends, indicating that as **Age** increases, the rate of depreciation changes, as measured by the decline in **Sale Price per Square Foot**. Rather than a fixed amount, the rate of depreciation slows as the property ages. To replicate this pattern, the linear equation $Y = a - b\,X$ has to be modified by adding a squared term, $c\,(X^2)$. The resulting equation is as follows:

Sale Price per Square Foot $= a - b$ (Age) $+ c$ (Age × Age)

The mechanics are simple: as **Age** increases, the negative trend represented by $-b$ (**Age**) is slowed by the positive term c (**Age** × **Age**). Figure 8.18 demonstrates this method of slowing the rate of depreciation.

> A *quadratic* equation is simply a linear equation with a squared term. Hence the traditional linear form $y = a + b\,X$ adds a squared term c (X^2) and becomes $y = a + b\,X + c\,(X^2)$.

Figure 8.17   Linear and Quadratic Trend Lines

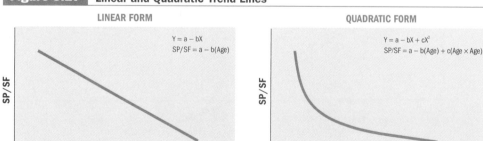

Complex relationships represented by non-linear functions may indicate two adjoining markets, as opposed to a single market (see Chapter 7). The appraiser needs to ensure that the framework of the analysis has been thorough enough to ensure that the market data is truly comparable to the subject.

The industrial data set is reduced to 94 sale properties with similar attributes, and the land value has been extracted. As can be seen, the data pattern appears to indicate a slowing in the decline per square foot as **Age** increases. Although a linear model would cross over most data points (indicated by the black line), a better model would have it bend slightly (indicated by the orange line). To replicate this form, a quadratic equation, which is a linear equation with an additional squared term, is necessary.

Model Calibration. Fortunately, the same SPSS linear regression routine in the previous examples can be used, but this time the equation includes a new variable, **Age2**, which represents **Age** × **Age**. Figure 8.19 shows the output relating to the fit and coefficient values of this model for depreciation. The R-square is a respectable 0.52801, which is sufficient given that only one valuation factor, **Age**, is being used. The output shown in Figure 8.20 includes a graphic representation of the regression line, which bends because of the squared term. (Remember that **Age2** is a squared version of **Age**.)

Figure 8.18   **Linear and Non-Linear Depreciation**

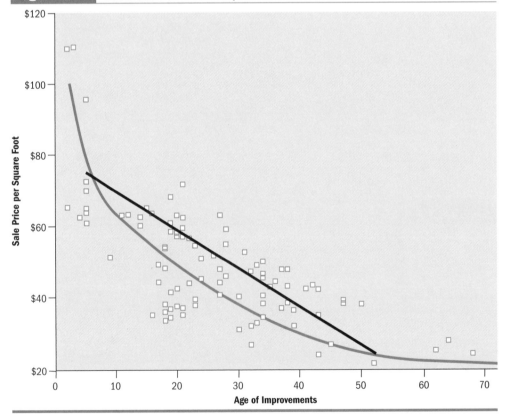

The orange line represents a line connecting all of the data points. The graph was produced using the SPSS routine Curve Estimation as part of the base regression routine. Based on the coefficients in the SPSS output, the formula for deprecation is

Sale Price per Square Foot = $79.27 − $1.616632 (**Age**) + .013361 (**Age** × **Age**)

Table 8.20 estimates the market-derived depreciation based on 10-year intervals using that equation.

The last three columns in the table provide a true market-based indication of depreciation reflected in the diminishing sale price per square foot, based on 94 sale properties. The totals are calculated using the depreciation function referenced in the second column. Column D is the sale price per square foot for each interval less the sale price per square foot for Year 0 ($79.27). Column E is the sale price per square foot at each interval divided by the sale price per square foot at Year 0, representing the cumulative depreciation. Column F is the annualized rate at each interval and is calculated by dividing the cumulative depreciation by the total number of years at each interval.

To apply the regression results in an appraisal, use the amount in column D against the total hard and soft costs (with profit) of the subject improvements. Dividing this amount by the total costs results in the percentage depreciation for the improvements. Column E provides an overall cumulative rate for the

---

Figure 8.19 | **SPSS Output**

Dependent variable.. SPSF Method.. QUADRATIC

Listwise Deletion of Missing Data

Multiple R .73359
R Square .53816
Adjusted R Square .52801
Standard Error 11.04708

　Analysis of Variance:

　DF Sum of Squares Mean Square

Regression 2 12940.556 6470.2778
Residuals 91 11105.452 122.0379

F = 53.01858 Signif F = .0000

-- Variables in the Equation --

Variable B SE B Beta T Sig T
AGE1 -1.616632 .263598 -1.381881 -6.133 .0000
AGE1**2 .013361 .004172 .721702 3.203 .0019
　(Constant) 79.273485 3.801641 20.852 .0000

Figure 8.20 — Sale Price per Square Foot by Improved Age

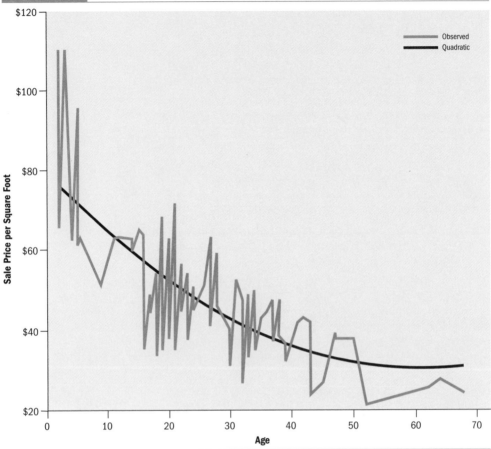

Table 8.20 — Market-derived Depreciation in 10-Year Intervals

A	B	C	D	E	F
		Sale Price	Depreciation	Depreciation	Annualized
Year	Model Equation	per Sq. Ft.	Amount	Rate	Depreciation
0	$\$79.27 - \$1.62\,(0) + \$.0134\,(0)^2$	$79.27	$0	0%	0%
10	$\$79.27 - \$1.62\,(10) + \$.0134\,(10)^2$	$64.41	$14.86	18.7%	1.9%
20	$\$79.27 - \$1.62\,(20) + \$.0134\,(20)^2$	$52.23	$27.04	34.1%	1.7%
30	$\$79.27 - \$1.62\,(30) + \$.0134\,(30)^2$	$42.73	$36.54	46.1%	1.5%
40	$\$79.27 - \$1.62\,(40) + \$.0134\,(40)^2$	$35.91	$43.36	54.7%	1.4%
50	$\$79.27 - \$1.62\,(50) + \$.0134\,(50)^2$	$31.77	$47.50	59.9%	1.2%
60	$\$79.27 - \$1.62\,(60) + \$.0134\,(60)^2$	$30.31	$48.96	61.8%	1.0%
70	$\$79.27 - \$1.62\,(70) + \$.0134\,(70)^2$	$31.53	$47.74	60.2%	0.9%

market. Likewise, Column F provides annualized deprecation factors. Both rates slow as age increases; in Column E, the depreciation function actually reverses slightly, indicating that the total useful life is between 60 and 70 years in this market.

The relationship is not perfect. Obviously, some properties are renovated throughout this period, and the appraisers must be sure that land values extracted are also market-supported and that there are no confounding variables masked by the variable **Age**. The model does, however, provide a good market-based depreciation analysis. Could this declining rate of depreciation be manually calculated without the quadratic regression function? The answer is yes. Using the same graph in SPSS (or its equivalent in Excel), the appraiser could manually plot segmented linear rates and calculate the rates with good approximation to the regression model above. This is similar to the manual options presented in Chapter 4. What is lost, however, are the statistical measures that tell the appraiser the overall fit of the model and the overall rate of decline in depreciation as properties age.

Figure 8.21 is identical to the previous graph. Rather than run a regression model against the data, the authors used a Lowess line to plot the quadratic trend line, and then manually created segmented straight lines by 10-year intervals to approximate the quadratic trend. The orange lines indicate the approximate intercepts on the y-axis to determine the sale price per square foot for every 10 years. The next step was to put this data into table form.

Table 8.21 provides a good approximation of the quadratic model, without the important statistical information provided by the latter. It is clearly superior to the "I think" approach to depreciation, however. It also provides users a good introduction to the applicability of this modeling process.

As a final step, the depreciation can now be provided using either of the models described above. The following example represents the subject property's cost approach summary:

Total costs of improvements (hard and soft costs)	$1,870,588
Add profit (@ 15%)	$280,588
Subtotal	$2,151,176
Less market-derived depreciation (30 years = 47.5%)	− $1,021,809
Depreciated costs of improvements	$1,129,367
Add land value (2 acres @ $175,000 per acre)*	$350,000
Valuation conclusion from cost approach	$1,479,367

* Calculated using a separate land valuation model

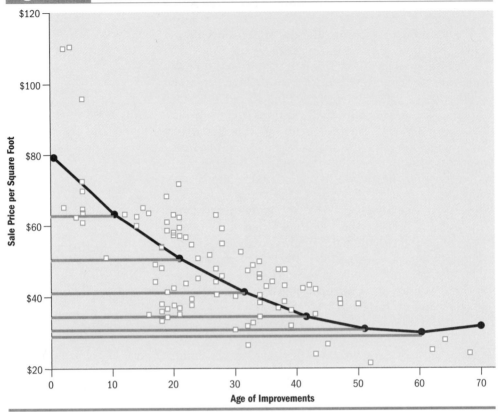

Figure 8.21 Manual Model Scatter Plot with Lowess Line

Table 8.21 Quadratic Model of Depreciation Estimation

A	C	D	E	F
Year	Sale Price per Square Foot	Depreciation Amount	Depreciation Rate	Annualized Depreciation
0	$80	$0	0%	0%
10	$62	$18	22.5%	2.3%
20	$49	$31	38.8%	1.9%
30	$42	$38	47.5%	1.6%
40	$35	$45	56.3%	1.4%
50	$32	$48	60.0%	1.2%
60	$31	$49	61.3%	1.0%
70	$31	$49	61.3%	0.9%

Conclusion

All three traditional approaches to value have provided similar value conclusions in the $1.2 to $1.5 million value range. This valuation started with more than 400 industrial sales that occurred over a four-year period. Final data sets for specific analyses were smaller, although the number of sales used was much greater than in the typical manual appraisal. Data was considered as a whole, and the specific properties eliminated were removed for sound appraisal reasons.

In narrative form, such analyses can guide the reader through the market and through the appraiser's thought processes. Another advantage is that much of this analysis could be applied to other appraisals. All of the data sets could be saved and applied to other property assignments as well. Updating the data would also be easy, given the ease of manipulation Excel, SPSS, and MiniTab provide to the user.

Given the length and depth of this chapter, the outline in Figure 8.22 is provided as a good overview and summary of appraisal valuation modeling using regression.

Figure 8.22   **AVMs Using Multiple Regression Analysis**

I. A statistical technique for estimating unknown data based on known and available data

II. Effective method of calibrating valuation models

III. Accurate models depend on:

  A. Adequate sales

  B. Consistent information on data analyzed

  C. Appropriate neighborhood or proximity variables

  D. Effective model building skills (basic knowledge of statistics is necessary)

IV. Applications

  A. Generally appropriate for residential properties in large and mid-sized communities

  B. Can be successful for commercial properties in large communities when sales are adequate

V. Strengths

  A. Directly rooted in the market

  B. Contains effective diagnostics for evaluating model accuracy

  C. Applications in all three approaches to value

  D. Abundant software available to perform analysis

VI. Limitations

  A. Produces poor values when data is inaccurate

  B. Requires adequate sales

  C. Values must be reviewed in field for accuracy

CHAPTER 9

Small Market Analysis

"Breathtaking. I shall call him 'Mini-Me'. . ."
–Mike Meyers, *Austin Powers: The Spy Who Shagged Me* (1999)

Throughout this book, sophisticated modeling procedures that can effectively manipulate large data sets with ease have been presented, but appraisers will always encounter situations where data is in short supply. Smaller rural markets or special-use properties present special challenges to appraisers using modeling procedures. These challenges are not insurmountable, though, if the appraiser can adjust the scope of the analysis.

Most statistical theory is based on behavioral sciences, which include economics and psychology. Many specific methods for dealing with uncertainty have sprung directly from psychology since there tends to be a great amount of uncertainty involving human behavior. In real estate analysis, much more of the equation is known. For example, while it is debatable that a person with two felony convictions is twice as "bad" as a person with one conviction, it is always true that a home of 2,000 square feet is twice as large as a home with an area of 1,000 square feet.

The greater degree of certainty in most real estate data can allow for a little more leeway in the statistical rules of thumb developed for other fields. For example, the old rule that cites a minimum of 30 observations for meaningful modeling is probably too high given that the appraiser can test output from small market models using empirical appraisal knowledge. For example, a model with only 20 sales can still be tested in the real world using appraisal judgment much more readily than a 20-person sample of convicted felons can be used in a major psychological study.

In addition, the cost of being wrong is not as high as, for example, it is in aircraft engineering. If the result of a modeling valuation is 20% more uncertain because a smaller set of data is used, the impact is far less life-threatening than a 20% uncertainty in tests for metal fatigue on commercial aircraft. This is not to downplay the constant effort to maintain measurable accuracy in appraisal and to increase reliability and validity. Remember, however, that the current state of analysis in appraisal involves sales data sets of less than 10 sales in too many instances. There are limitations to modeling smaller data sets. Appraisers need to be prepared to model using small data sets, but they should always strive to include as much market data as possible.

Case Study: Mount Sopris Neighborhood

In this case study, a small residential market from a Western Slope community in Colorado was examined. The market had a total of 16 sales. The purpose of setting up the appraisal valuation model was to determine the probable market value of single-family homes within this market.

Mount Sopris was developed during the early 1970s and contains approximately 150 homes. The location is south of an urban area in rural western Colorado. Although benefiting from the proximity to a major regional center, the subject neighborhood is still several miles away and separated by a railroad track and a river. In addition, the type and age of these homes are much different than the typical residential product within the town. The appraisers decided to develop a residential model for the valuation of homes in this neighborhood because they receive numerous appraisal assignments concerning property there. There have been 16 sales of these homogenous (i.e., very similar) homes over the prior 24 months; the last sale occurred six months ago. The histograms in Figure 9.1 illustrate several significant housing attributes:

- In the neighborhood, sale price per square foot, size of homes, and ages of homes are homogenous (i.e., similar).
- The sales activity appears to have been fairly steady through most of the eight-month sale period.

In the model specification phase of EDA, the appraisers chose an additive regression model that predicts the total sale price of each property. This choice was based on the comparison of the COVs of two candidates for dependent variable in the model, the sale price per square foot and the total sale price.

Figure 9.1 **Attributes of Residential Sales**

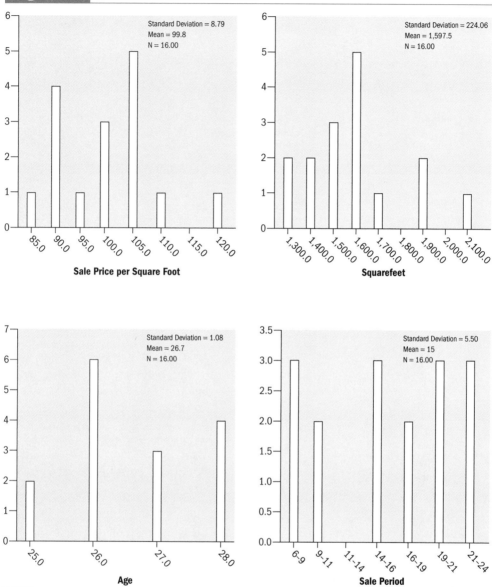

The regression model included the variables shown in Table 9.1. Of the variables (the dependent variable is shaded), several probably should have been excluded outright because they had no variation (i.e., no values). The last three variables indicated the type of garage. It turns out that all homes had attached garages. Given the harsh climate of this region, there were no evaporative coolers, detached garages, or carports, which makes appraisal sense.

With smaller market models, the authors typically adjust the significance threshold in SPSS. Also

Table 9.1	Descriptive Statistics		
	Mean	**Standard Deviation**	**N**
Saleamt	158334.38	16516.070	16
Squarefeet	1597.50	224.058	16
Bsmtsf	914.81	377.515	16
Bathrooms	2.8125	.44253	16
Carspaces	2.06	.250	16
Fireplaces	.81	.655	16
Lotsize	9996.88	1230.603	16
Age	26.6875	1.07819	16
Sale period	15.44	5.501	16
Evap. cooler	.0000	.00000	16
Detached garage	.0000	.00000	16
Carport	.0000	.00000	16
Attached garage	1.0000	.00000	16

The t value is simply the coefficient value divided by the standard error of the coefficient. The larger the t value, the better. The corresponding p (i.e., probability) value reflects the probability that the coefficient value is spurious and the independent variable does not contribute to the equation. The smaller the p value is, the better. Since p is a function of t, as t increases in value p diminishes.

P-value standards are based on testing the hypothesis that the phenomenon observed is a result of random chance. The 0.05 limit was developed by R.A. Fischer, a famous English statistician. He chose the 0.05 level because a competing statistical school chose a limit of 0.10 for their significance levels. Thus, to a statistical neophyte Fischer's analyses could be misinterpreted as being "twice" as accurate.

called the *tolerance limit*, this threshold is automatically set at 0.05, meaning that during the stepwise process, the regression model uses this limit to determine whether a variable is added, removed, or kept out of the model. At every step, the regression model will add the next most significant independent variable based on the t value, which is the statistic tested for significance. The first step includes the variable with the highest t value, which will therefore have the lowest significance level below 0.05. Again, the interpretation of this process is that as a model adds variables, the R-square increases. The test determines whether the added variable is statistically adding legitimate explanatory power to the model. The basis of this legitimacy is the t statistic for that variable; its significance tells the model that the likelihood is low (i.e., less than 0.05 or 5%) that the variable's relationship to the dependent variable is due to random chance.

For small market models, appraisers can set this threshold level much higher, often at 0.30 or even higher. The smaller amount of data tends to make the 0.05 threshold too restrictive. Sometimes at that significance level no variables can be entered into the model. Appraisers have a very strong ability to determine the soundness of the coefficients used in the model even with higher thresholds. Again, remember that these limits were developed for *other* fields of study. Appraisers have much less uncertainty about the validity of the coefficient values based on a significant body of appraisal knowledge. In the model example here, the initial tolerance limit was set at

0.30 for variables entering the model and 0.31 for variables removed from the model.

The regression model had to be recalibrated several times. While the first runs were strong in terms of the COV, there were problems with several coefficients. The following step-by-step description of the model calibration removed these problem variables over several regression runs. Please note that each run used a stepwise process. The final steps are presented for each run, as shown in Table 9.2.

The model had excellent statistical accuracy (low standard error, high R-square), but two valuation factors, **AC** (air-conditioning) and **Finbsmtsf** (finished basement square feet), were negative. They were likely interacting with other variables (i.e., creating a multicollinearity problem). For the next run (Table 9.3), both variables were removed.

| Table 9.2 | Model Run 1 |

Model Summary

Model	R	R-Square	Adjusted R-Square	Standard Error of the Estimate
1	.778(a)	.605	.577	10738.344
2	.836(b)	.699	.653	9735.731
3	.870(c)	.757	.696	9105.225
4	.922(d)	.850	.795	7468.917
5	.933(e)	.871	.807	7260.609
6	.945(f)	.893	.822	6962.081

a. Predictors: (Constant), Squarefeet

b. Predictors: (Constant), Squarefeet, Monthrel

c. Predictors: (Constant), Squarefeet, Monthrel, Fireplaces

d. Predictors: (Constant), Squarefeet, Monthrel, Fireplaces, AC

e. Predictors: (Constant), Squarefeet, Monthrel, Fireplaces, AC, Bathrooms

f. Predictors: (Constant), Squarefeet, Monthrel, Fireplaces, AC, Bathrooms, Finbsmtsf

Coefficients (a)

Model		Unstandardized Coefficients		Standardized Coefficients	T	Sig.
		B	Standard Error	Beta		
6	(Constant)	76424.604	17520.320		4.362	.002
	Squarefeet	45.065	8.513	.611	5.293	.000
	Monthrel	-1209.506	340.436	-.403	-3.553	.006
	Fireplaces	9833.976	3230.888	.390	3.044	.014
	AC	-13214.330	5260.166	-.323	-2.512	.033
	Bathrooms	10551.416	5577.284	.283	1.892	.091
	Finbsmtsf	-8.753	6.391	-.216	-1.370	.204

a. Dependent Variable: Saleamt

Table 9.3 — Model Run 2

Model Summary

Model	R	R-Square	Adjusted R-Square	Standard Error of the Estimate
1	.778(a)	.605	.577	10738.344
2	.836(b)	.699	.653	9735.731
3	.870(c)	.757	.696	9105.225
4	.885(d)	.783	.704	8985.565

a. Predictors: (Constant), Squarefeet
b. Predictors: (Constant), Squarefeet, Monthrel
c. Predictors: (Constant), Squarefeet, Monthrel, Fireplaces
d. Predictors: (Constant), Squarefeet, Monthrel, Fireplaces, Bsmtsf

Coefficients (a)

Model		Unstandardized Coefficients		Standardized Coefficients	T	Sig.
		B	Standard Error	Beta		
4	(Constant)	86629.813	18484.310		4.687	.001
	Squarefeet	55.922	10.614	.759	5.269	.000
	Monthrel	-1062.429	427.951	-.354	-2.483	.030
	Fireplaces	6651.360	3630.361	.264	1.832	.094
	Bsmtsf	-7.251	6.307	-.166	-1.150	.275

a. Dependent Variable: Saleamt

Median-based statistical procedures, called *non-parametric* tests, can be used in place of parametric (mean-based) procedures, especially if the data is unstable (i.e., has too much variance). Keep in mind, however, that the data may be so unstable that the model will not run properly no matter what is done in the model specification and calibration procedures.

In this run, the R-square dropped to 0.704 and the standard error increased to $8,986. Dividing the standard error by the mean sale price ($8,986 / $158,334) resulted in a COV of 5.7%, still very low. At this point, the tolerance limit was increased in SPSS to 0.20 for the third run of the model (Table 9.4), given that the coefficient for **Bsmtsf** (basement square feet) was negative and its significance was 0.275.

In the final model run, the excluded variables shown in Table 9.5 are included to the model output for illustration purposes only. All the coefficients that were still in the model are defensible from an appraisal perspective, and the model retains significant accuracy. The excluded variables had either odd values or were simply not significant, even with the less restrictive threshold. Note too that in general, the less statistical significance an independent variable exhibits, the more its relative predictive power in the model decreases. So excluding an insignificant variable generally does not hurt the model. In this case, the COV was a very strong 5.8% and the R-square was 0.696; approximately 70% of the variation was explained by this model.

| Table 9.4 | Model Run 3 |

Model Summary

Model	R	R-Square	Adjusted R-Square	Standard Error of the Estimate
1	.778(a)	.605	.577	10738.344
2	.836(b)	.699	.653	9735.731
3	.870(c)	.757	.696	9105.225

a. Predictors: (Constant), Squarefeet

b. Predictors: (Constant), Squarefeet, Monthrel

c. Predictors: (Constant), Squarefeet, Monthrel, Fireplaces

Coefficients (a)

Model		Unstandardized Coefficients		Standardized Coefficients	T	Sig.
		B	Standard Error	Beta		
3	(Constant)	83040.550	18461.365		4.498	.001
	Squarefeet	53.871	10.602	.731	5.081	.000
	Monthrel	-1022.827	432.243	-.341	-2.366	.036
	Fireplaces	6185.320	3655.700	.245	1.692	.116

a. Dependent Variable: Saleamt

| Table 9.5 | Excluded Variables (d) |

Model		Beta In	t	Sig.	Partial Correlation	Collinearity Statistics
						Tolerance
3	Bsmtsf	-.166(c)	-1.150	.275	-.328	.949
	Bathrooms	.109(c)	.690	.505	.204	.853
	Carspaces	.111(c)	.702	.498	.207	.853
	Lotsize	.001(c)	.003	.998	.001	.689
	Age	-.148(c)	-.951	.362	-.276	.838

a. Predictors in the Model: (Constant), Squarefeet

b. Predictors in the Model: (Constant), Squarefeet, Monthrel

c. Predictors in the Model: (Constant), Squarefeet, Monthrel, Fireplaces

d. Dependent Variable: Saleam

General Guidelines

Appraisers can model smaller markets with success, but caution must be exercised at each step. In larger data sets, the law of large numbers can offset problems with individual data points. In smaller data sets, however, every sale must be carefully checked for accuracy and market veracity. In larger data sets, sale verification is less important because problem sales tend to fall out or are removed during the exploratory data analysis stage. Appraisers should personally verify a sample of the sales in a large data set, but for small data sets *all* of the sales should be verified.

Small data sets are much more prone to influence from outlier sales. These sales need to be carefully evaluated, and the cost of excluding them needs to be weighed against the influence they may exert if left in the model. Sale properties with missing variables, which would be excluded outright in larger data sets, may need to be left in to provide sufficient sale numbers. The appraiser may have to replace the missing value with a proxy value (such as the mean or median value of the range of values for that variable), or the variable itself may have to be removed. Note that SPSS and MiniTab both exclude an entire data point if one of its variables has a missing value.

There are no clear benchmarks for many of these modeling questions. In the case study example, the data was homogenous; 16 observations were "enough" data to effectively model the neighborhood. Often this is not the case, and the model performance is poor. Of course, appraisers can augment the model output with manually derived adjustments for valuation factors not in the model or removed from the model because of multicollinearity problems. Appraisers need to keep in mind that the problems with the model may also be present in a manual adjustment grid using traditional appraisal approaches.

To transfer a valuation equation from a model to a traditional grid is simple. For example, consider the industrial valuation model used in Chapter 8 for the sales comparison approach. The valuation equation shown in Figure 9.2 was derived from the original direct sales comparison analysis, with two additional variables added in a manual adjustment grid.

With the adjustments in place, the adjusted sale price is $1.35 million, somewhat below the conclusion of $1.5 million (rounded) from the model itself using the sales comparison approach. With the conversion grid totals, the appraiser can now use these adjustments in a manual grid and add one or more additional variables.

Other remedies to smaller market data sets can include the combining of several smaller markets using cluster analysis, combining different property classes, and the inclusion of rental properties as sale proxies. All of these require a thorough knowledge of these techniques and the markets themselves.

In some smaller markets, there is great overlap between property classes. Commercial and industrial properties competing for the same limited land supply often exhibit sale attributes that are similar, allowing for the combination of these classes.

Figure 9.2   Adjustment Process

Value = $26.29 (Size) + $2,665 (Parking spaces) + $8,318 (Office finish) + $20,905 (Truss height)

Note: Constant = 0 and Market Trend = 0

Conversion Grid				
Valuation Factor	**Comp 1**	**Subject**	**Adjustment Calculations (Whole Dollar)**	**Percentage Adjustment**
Size	20,000	30,000	(30,000 − 20,000) × $26.29 = $262,900	$262,900 / $1,000,000 = +26%
Parking spaces	30	50	(50 − 30) × $2,665 = $53,300	$53,300 / $1,000,000 = +5%
Office finish	10%	20%	(20 − 10) × $8,318 = $83,180	$83,180 / $1,000,000 = +8%
Truss height	22	20	(20 − 22) × $20,905 = -$41,810	-$41,810 / $1,000,000 = -4%

Manual Adjustment Grid									
Sale	**Sale Price**	**Market Trend**	**Size**	**Parking Spaces**	**Office Finish**	**Truss Height**	**Adjust. 1**	**Adjust. 2**	**Adjusted Sale Price**
1	$1,000,000	0%	+26%	+5%	+8%	-4%	?	?	$???

Conclusion

The use of appraisal valuation modeling in smaller markets is challenging, but the whole market rationale for using it applies as it does in larger markets. The need to convey all of the market information is critical in smaller markets. Outlier data and missing data need to be carefully evaluated and used if at all possible. The statistical parameters guiding the modeling process can be relaxed, but appraisers need to realize that they do not have a multitude of data to offset the effects of outliers or spurious data. Coefficients for valuation factors must be carefully evaluated against appraisal theory and empirical data.

Great benefits can accrue, however, from AVM use in smaller markets. More objectivity can be maintained in the adjustment process, and statistical data supporting the valuation can be provided as well. Overall, the strengths described in Chapter 1 apply to both smaller and larger markets.

CHAPTER 10

Evaluating the Valuers

"I'm your huckleberry . . ."

–Val Kilmer, as the defiant and doomed
Doc Holliday, *Tombstone* (1993)

At the present time, members of the appraisal and banking professions have abrogated their responsibilities for the oversight and review of the AVM technology being developed. The lending profession, in concert with a small group of AVM providers, has been driving automated valuation. If appraisers fail to take the initiative to provide significant input into the evaluation of vendor-supplied automated valuation products, they may, in effect, hasten their own obsolescence.

This chapter defines what appraisers can do at the local level and how they can identify the strengths and weaknesses of AVM products on the market. This process begins with evaluation of the appraiser's own appraisal valuation models, which were examined in previous chapters. In addition, important terms will be presented to define critical analyses that can be used to determine when AVMs work and when they do not.

In previous chapters, evaluation tools such as the R-square and COV statistics were examined and demonstrated as effective initial measures of modeling accuracy. Other statistics, such as the chi-square and f-statistic, have not been referenced because in most instances appraisers will not need their services in evaluating appraisal valuation models.

The purpose of most AVMs on the market is to predict the value of residential properties. Other model applications have different stated goals, but all have the ultimate goal of determining either directly or indirectly the market value of a single residential property. All models also have one thing in common: they take market data of some kind and develop valuation output of some kind. The output may be a market value estimate, a rental income estimate, or a depreciation estimate, but all of these relate to value

With all this new technology in place, how can we know that AVM techniques really work? Who is qualified to review the appropriateness of the data considered, the techniques applied, or the accuracy of the conclusions reached?

in some way. This output is good when it is accurate, and it is not as good when it is less accurate.

Accuracy

Accuracy is one of the important determinants of model quality. Three critical elements affect the accuracy of a model:

- Validity
- Reliability
- Precision

Validity concerns whether the AVM output really is what it says it is. For example, in the depreciation model presented in Chapter 8, are the rates really depreciation rates or are they masking other valuation factors? Is the market trend model really deriving the monthly inflation or deflation rate, or is it measuring the impact of a new subdivision that has flooded the market with new, upscale product? Is location truly based on the location of the sale properties, or is it a proxy for quality? Is the reported market value really market value, or is it a retail value for individual buyers? All of these questions concerning the ability to demonstrate that a model's result is what it says it is fall under the category of validity. If a model is not valid, then its accuracy is irrelevant. A plane's navigation system that mistakenly identifies a mountain as a canyon is of less than no use, even if the location of said canyon is accurate.

How is validity measured in an AVM product? It is measured through appraisal evaluation of the AVM's model specifications. If the model is set up incorrectly for a market, then it cannot truly answer the appraisal question. AVM products must demonstrate that they are employing the correct unit of measure and contain the proper elements of comparison for the property valuation. There must be a way to review the valuation algorithm (i.e., equation) to ensure that the proper variables are included.

The second element affecting accuracy, *reliability*, is the ability of a model to be repeated with the same or similar results using different sets of data. The goal of a valuation model is to predict market behavior. If the model cannot repeat the valuation process under similar conditions, then is it reasonable to expect any market transactions to be correctly modeled in the first place? In most instances, the issues of reliability concerns whether unsold properties are treated the same as sold properties in the model. Do the sales used reflect the entire population of properties? Are there subclasses of unsold properties that are excluded or misinterpreted by the AVM?

The final element of accuracy is *precision.* Overly precise model conclusions were discussed in a previous chapter, but in this case the ability of a model to measure market behavior in a meaningful way is in question. For example, is the functional form of the model correct for the specific market? Are additive models correctly interpreting the market transaction mechanism? If homes are purchased in a market and five basic valuation factors are used by market participants to set prices and purchase homes, does the AVM correctly model this market?

Testing Model Accuracy

The validity, reliability, and precision of the model are all important, and they must be examined to determine the accuracy of a model. If tests of any one of these elements fail, then the model will fail. Demonstrable accuracy involves more than just a good R-square provided by the vendor. It requires a proper model for the evaluation of accuracy, similar to Figure 10.1. This model can be used to evaluate individual output or the entire AVM system. The principles are the same in either case.

Figure 10.1 **Testing AVM Output for Accuracy**

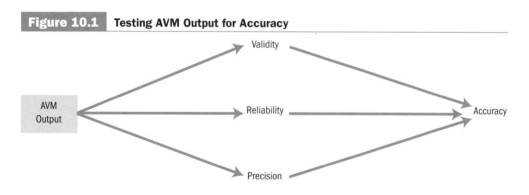

Output statistics and sales ratio analysis can determine the precision of the model, but in general a less reliable, valid, and precise model will have poorer output statistics.

The statistical tools used to determine accuracy include ratio measures, measure of statistical fit, and tests for sold and unsold deviation. Any evaluation that does not address these three factors cannot effectively determine if a model (or an entire AVM system) is truly accurate.

R-Square Versus COV

Selecting evaluation statistics depends on the goal of the analysis. If the goal is to examine property valuation conclusions, then statistics such as the COV and COD are preferred over general statistical measures of fit such as R-square. The former statistics provide a good indication of the average error, while the latter provide good evaluative measures for the entire model. The appraiser needs to know how to evaluate the strengths and weaknesses of each group of statistics. There are instances when one will be preferred over another; in general, COV evaluation is superior to goodness-of-fit statistics for single-property valuation.

The R-square statistic (known by many names such as the *measurement of association, measurement of dispersion,* and others) is the ratio of the variance explained by the model divided by the total variance within the data. Hence, the calculations result in a ratio that is easily converted into a percentage (0.85 to 85%). It ranges from 0%, meaning no variance is explained by the model (which is bad), to 100%, which means all the variance is explained by the model (which is ideal). Recall that variance is the association between two or more variables. In the following example, a simple *bivariate* (i.e., two-variable) relationship is used so it can be graphed easily. The same principles apply to three or more variables as well.

Figure 10.2 illustrates the R-square relationship. The regression model creates a line that travels through the set of data points based on the total minimum squared distance between the line and each point. The dotted lines are the errors—that is, the distance between the actual values and the values estimated by the regression line. Note that some of the dotted lines are above the regression line and some are below. Adding up the distances of those lines should total zero because some points are above the line (i.e., positive) and some are below (negative). To measure the total variance, the regression process squares these dotted lines to make all of them positive. Does this sound familiar? It should. It is the same process used to calculate the formula for the standard deviation in Chapter 3. It is also the same process used to calculate ANOVA in Chapter 4. The term *sum of squares* refers to this process.

The orange bracket indicates the total variance for a particular data point. The orange line represents the variation accounted for by the regression

There are many excellent explanations of the R-square available in texts or other sources. It is beyond the scope of this book to go too far into the theoretical underpinnings of this well-known statistical measure. The R-square and regression modeling go hand in hand because, if properly set up and calibrated, the R-square provides an excellent and easily comparative measure of the overall fit of a model. The appraiser can evaluate the model using the R-square by itself (closer to 100% is better), or different models can be compared (those closer to 100% are better than those that are not).

Figure 10.2 R-Square in Linear Regression

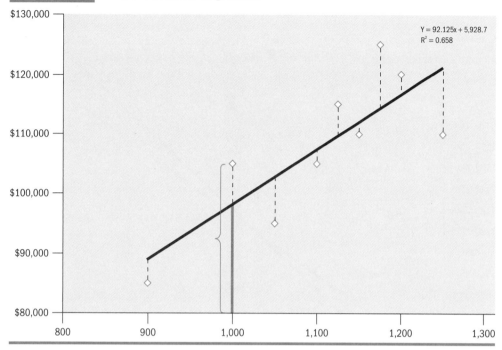

$Y = 92.125x + 5,928.7$
$R^2 = 0.658$

line (explained variation), while the dotted line represents what is not accounted for (unexplained variation, or *error*). The R-square ratio is the total dotted lines divided by the orange brackets over the whole range of values.

The line is centered at the mean x-axis value and the mean y-axis value. Because distances are squared, the values at the ends of the line exert much more influence on the regression model than those toward the center. If an extreme outlier value is added at either end, the line is affected significantly, but the R-square can actually increase because, with the new extreme value, the total squared differences increase and the line tries to minimize the total differences. It therefore pivots to the new extreme value, as shown in Figure 10.3.

To account for the extreme value, the regression line tilts up greatly (a slope of 177 versus 92 in the previous graph), and the R-square increases greatly. This is a result of the strong influence of the sale for $200,000. Since the regression model builds the line based on the squared differences for both the x- and y-axes about the mean values for both (represented by the orange circle), the squared difference for the outlier sale overwhelms the regression line. Yet, when the R-square statistic is calculated, it actually

Figure 10.3   Outlier Efffect on R-Square

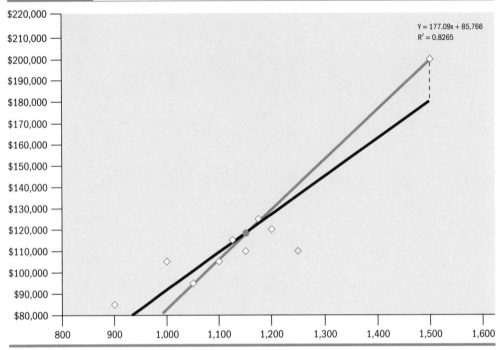

improves because the model looks at all distances squared. The increased distances for all the other data points are more than outweighed by the relatively narrow distance for this new extreme sale. The overall model, however, is inferior.

The COV is the standard deviation of the dotted lines divided by the mean value of y in the above model, so the COV can move in the opposite direction of the R-square. The standard deviation of the dotted lines (the standard error) in Figure 10.2 is $7,674; dividing this by the mean sale price of $107,778 results in a COV of 7.1%. When the same calculation is performed for the second example, with the extreme value, the standard deviation of the error lines is $13,863 and the mean value is $117,000, resulting in a COV of 11.8%. Because the standard error is affected by the squared distance between the regression line and the actual value, the COV will decrease, even though the R-square actually goes up. As noted earlier, the model is inferior in the second case, even with the higher R-square ratio.

If this analysis had not been performed, which model would have been selected based on the two measures of model accuracy? Most analysts would have likely preferred the second model with the much superior R-square statistic, even though the correct selection would have been the first model with the superior COV. Again, this conclusion assumes the goal is a point estimate and that the data set has been properly edited and prepared. It also assumes that the size of the subject property falls in the middle range of the sales data. If the subject was similar to the outlier sale, then the entire model would have to be called into question.

The COV is relevant because it uses the actual dimensions of the dependent variable in its calculation. The R-square is a dimensionless ratio statistic; it has relevance as a general measure of fit, but it should never be considered over the COV if the goal is to estimate individual property values. AVM output must provide COV data, or some equivalent, along with any statistical measures of fit. As can be seen, the use of the R-square by itself is not sufficient.

Ratio Analysis

Once the overall statistical fit is established, the next step is to examine the output for further outlier influence, patterns in the errors, and progressiveness or regressiveness. All of these factors can be examined with ratio analysis, using the ratios of the predicted y value over the actual y value. In most AVMs, this indicates the predicted sale price divided by the actual sale price. Appraisers need to be comfortable with this easy and practical application tool. A whole host of graphical analyses can be performed, and some of these tools have already been used in previous regression modeling applications in this book.

As noted earlier, the sales ratio method offers an easy way to verify the accuracy of an AVM. Of course, the entire output of sale properties is needed to perform a ratio-based verification, but if the AVM uses an appraiser's own data, this is straightforward. An appraiser asked by a client to verify the accuracy of a vendor AVM, however, will need to get the output from the vendor to perform the following steps.

The first step in ratio analysis has already been demonstrated. Using graphs and developing the COD and COV, either in SPSS or in Excel, provides a simple way to verify how the ratios are clustered and their central tendencies. As noted, the ratios represent the errors in the model. Error terms are measured either above or below the value 1.0, which is a perfect fit. Both box and whisker plots and scatter plots provide good graphical representations of the pattern of the errors. The ratio analysis provides statistics such as the COV, COD, and PRD as well as the mean and median ratio values, which should be very close to 1.0.

When is the R-square statistic more relevant than the COV? Typically it is preferred in a portfolio analysis, where the valuation assignment is to value all properties in the portfolio in aggregate. In this case, the point estimate accuracy is less relevant than the overall fit of the valuation model.

Ratio means and medians should always be close to 1.0 because that is the ratio where the predicted value equals the actual value.

Using the output from the analysis of deprecia-tion in Chapter 8 provides a good overview of these basic output tools (Table 10.1 and Figure 10.4). The output table from Ratios in SPSS provides a summa-ry of the COV, COD, and other statistics. Of note—and verified by Chart A—is the skewed nature of the ratios. The mean of 1.05 and median of 1.0 indicate the skewed right distribution. The COV is over 20%, while the COD is 18.1%. While acceptable for com-mercial models, this level of variance in the error terms would be unacceptable for residential models.

Table 10.1	Ratio Statistics for Unstandardized Predicted Value/Sale Price per Square Foot	
Mean		1.051
Median		1.001
Minimum		.728
Maximum		1.662
Standard deviation		.229
Range		.934
Price-related differential		1.035
Coefficient of dispersion		.181
Coefficient of variation	(mean-centered)	21.8%
	(median-centered)	23.4%
Coefficient of concentration	(within 50% of median inclusive)	95.7%

Chart B in Figure 10.4 allows for easy comparison between independent variables or even variables not in the model, using box and whisker plots, which also compare the distribution of the ratios and median val-ues. In this chart, the properties located in Denver account for nearly 50% of the sales and provide for a symmetrical distribution around a median of slightly over 1.0. The next largest market, Englewood (an older, adjacent suburban city), has a median slightly less than 1.0. Commerce City may present a problem for this model given that most of its ratios are above 1.0. The appraiser would want to examine why this market is not being modeled properly.

Chart C provides a scatter plot of the ratios and sale prices. The PRD of 1.03 indicates slight regres-sive tendencies of this model, which the scatter plot appears to support.

With this information and other ratio analyses, the appraiser can compare the ratios across all inde-pendent variables, using the box and whisker plots for categorical data and binary variables. Any pattern in the ratios may indicate that further calibration of

Figure 10.4 SPSS Output

CHART A

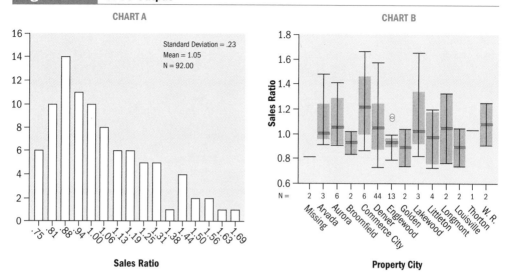

Standard Deviation = .23
Mean = 1.05
N = 92.00

Sales Ratio

CHART B

Sales Ratio

Property City

CHART C

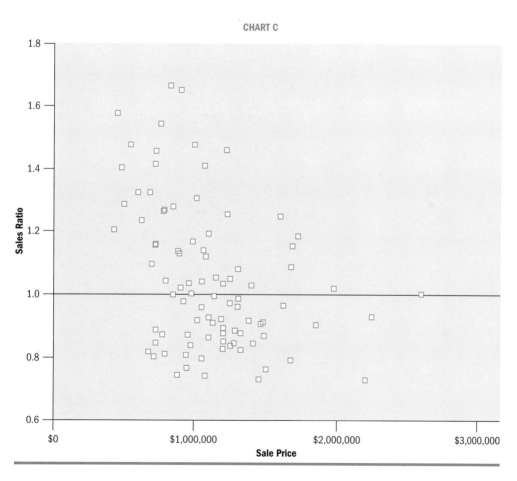

Sales Ratio

Sale Price

the model is required. For example, a variable that had been excluded previously may have to be reinstated into the model. Categories that were combined in the model coding may have to be broken out again.

Testing Data

For years the assessment community has dealt with AVM accuracy. As used in legislative regulations governing assessment, the terms *level of assessment* and *equalization* refer to the accuracy of mass appraisal models based on ratio analysis. The level of assessment in many jurisdictions is required to be no more than a certain percentage (plus or minus) from 1.0. In addition, the dispersion about the mean or median, as measured by the COV, COD, or both, must also be within limits established by the jurisdiction. Most of these thresholds are based on standards for mass appraisal valuation set forth by the International Association of Assessing Officers (IAAO), the professional organization equivalent to the Appraisal Institute for assessment appraisers.

In addition to threshold standards based on sales ratios, the assessment community also tests for the valuation equivalence of sold and unsold property. It is one thing for a mass appraisal model to correctly value sale properties, but this does not address the unsold properties that are also being valued. This has a direct corollary in the single-property appraisal world because many appraised properties are not for sale at the time of the appraisal. The unequal treatment of sold versus unsold properties in a mass appraisal model is known by the assessment branch of appraisal as *chasing sales*. It is a highly descriptive term because some models accurately value sold properties but fail to accurately value the majority of properties that do not sell.

Of the testing methods applied to measure for unequal valuation, several require a former valuation based on the prior assessment period. However, there are several methods that single-property appraisers could use to verify these mass appraisal vendor AVMs. One method is to apply a base valuation model to the sold properties in the model and then test this against properties that have not sold. This could involve the entire data set of properties in the AVM, or it could use samples from each group of properties. If the AVM property is not retrospective (i.e., the values have already been calculated), where values are produced on demand, the vendor would have to supply a current sample of values for a set amount of sold and unsold properties. The base model would use a preselected set of variables to value the properties. The goal would not be to replicate the AVM-generated values but to test for equality between sold and unsold properties.

A variant method would be to randomly select 10% of the sale properties and exclude them from the initial AVM modeling. The holdout sample could then be tested using the same model to verify that there is no bias present. This method is effective for appraisers verifying their own models. Using this strategy to verify a commercial vendor AVM would require an agreement with the vendor to exclude sales for the holdout sample. The vendor would not select the sales for the sample for obvious reasons.

This leads to the most critical issue of AVM verification—third-party involvement. Currently, users of AVMs are provided output statistics to verify the accuracy of the AVM. This is tantamount to a service provider telling their client that the product works because they say it works. Third-party verification is critical. Data from the AVM should be available in the form described above to verify accuracy, but not from the same firm supplying the AVM itself. In many assessment jurisdictions, this third-party verification is a legislative requirement. In Colorado, for example, a private firm is contracted to audit the valuation and assessment practices of county assessors. The authors believe that this type of verification is critical in the private sector too as the market is increasingly impacted by AVM encroachment. This may provide a new field of work for appraisal firms with the foresight to pursue such projects over the next several years.

CHAPTER 11

Steps to Competence

"He is intelligent but not experienced. His pattern indicates two-dimensional thinking."

–Mr. Spock, *Star Trek II: The Wrath of Kahn* (1982)

Statistics as it is often taught can be a discouraging exercise, to say the least, so the resistance of single-property appraisers to the use of statistical analysis is understandable and somewhat forgivable. This cannot go on, however, in light of industry trends and new technology. Appraisers must become competent using modeling techniques to remain competitive and compliant with industry standards.

Nowhere is this more evident than in the outright rejection of a simple statistical measure: the mean. For years, appraisers have been taught to reject averages as a way of evaluating data. This is highly outdated thinking. With even a manual adjustment grid, there is no appraisal reason *not* to go to the mean, unless one or more of the comparable sales (or rents) are demonstrably more comparable than the others. As long as the appraiser describes the process that leads to the conclusion that all of the comparable properties are relatively similar, the mean or median adjustment unit value should be acceptable.

Within the formalized training and curriculum of fee appraisers, statistical analysis and techniques continue to be regarded as add-on methods. Often statistical methods are not even addressed; students are provided with formulas to calculate the mean or standard deviation on their calculators. This type of instruction may actually lead some appraisers to simply avoid modeling and statistical analysis altogether.

Statistical Analysis in Appraisal Literature

The twelfth edition of *The Appraisal of Real Estate*, while not overwhelming in its endorsement of statistical methodology, does support much of what the authors have contended in this book. Relevant sections of that textbook are quoted here.

The private fee branch of the appraisal profession has been historically reluctant to embrace statistics. In fact, the reverse has often described the attitude of appraisal practitioners. Some simply fail to use these techniques, but other private sector appraisers have expressed distaste for statistical analysis, preferring instead to extract every physical and economic characteristic relevant to the valuation process from a distillation of a limited number of comparable sales.

The admonition against "going to the average" would also preclude the use of regression analysis because the least squares model is based on mean values of the dependent and independent variables.

Statistical Analysis

Statistical methods can sometimes be applied to calculate adjustments to comparable sales. To apply any statistical analysis, the appraiser must be familiar with (and properly apply) fundamental statistical concepts as well as the particular methodology selected. In applying statistical analysis, the appraiser must be careful not to develop a result that is mathematically precise yet meaningless or inappropriate for the particular appraisal.

As an example, an appraiser may develop size adjustments for various sizes of land but not have a size adjustment for a parcel that is sufficiently comparable to the subject property to warrant the use of the adjustment. By creating a simple linear regression model, the appraiser may develop a series of adjustment factors for differing tract sizes and use the result as a means of inferring the size adjustment for properties within the range of the data. If there is a reasonable pattern, it can be applied to a group of sales with differing land sizes to test its likely accuracy, although the process might also demonstrate that the adjustments compared are incorrect. The results of this process may be closer to qualitative analysis than a direct quantitative adjustment, but market support for the adjustment can be produced in this way.

Appraisers should recognize the differences between statistical processes in the collection and description of data and should be able to distinguish between descriptive and inferential statistics. Without an understanding of the issues, any use of statistical calculations is dangerous or ill-advised. For example, some appraisers extract adjustments for direct sales comparison processes directly from multiple regression analyses, without recognizing that regression studies do not develop indications of causation but rather of associations between and among independent variables and a dependent (or predicted) variable such as sales price. It is entirely improper to mix a value of a single regression coefficient that is developed for a given statistical model with other market adjustments developed from paired sales analysis or other market data comparison techniques.

Graphic Analysis

Graphic analysis is a variant of statistical analysis in which the appraiser arrives at a conclusion by visually interpreting a graphic display of data and applying statistical curve fit analysis. A simple graphic display of grouped data may illustrate how the market reacts to variations in the elements of comparison or may reveal submarket trends. In curve fit analysis, different formulas may be employed to determine the best fit for the market data being analyzed. The most reliable equation for the best fit curve can be plotted, or the most appropriate equation of those commonly used to solve for an adjustment can be identified.[1]

The signals given are mixed. First, the reader is told that statistical methods can be applied "sometimes" as part of the appraisal process. Next, the reader is advised against misapplying statistical methods unless properly skilled (a point with which the authors agree). The example provided seems to contradict the admonition in the third paragraph against mixing coefficient adjustments from a simple regression model with another market adjustment. The authors do not disagree with the adjustment derived for the differing land tracts (which is similar to our scale adjustment example), but we do think deriving an adjustment from a simple linear regression model and then using it with other market-derived adjustments is acceptable. As noted, any adjustment based on paired sales data should be used as a last resort.

Common Misunderstandings

Anecdotal evidence abounds in the misunderstandings involving descriptive and inferential analysis. A review appraiser, in analyzing certain information provided within an appraisal report, noted that "the appraiser had gone so far as to mention the average of a data set, a clear violation of the guidelines of USPAP." When a profession rejects the very analytical tools that can assist in evaluating data, it rejects the understanding of this data and its relevancy.

When appraisers had limited amounts of data, they could get away with limited analysis, replacing it with appraisal judgment. Confronted with the abundance of data now available, appraisers can no longer dismiss the very real insights that data can provide within the valuation process. In fact, there is such a significant amount of data available that some have suggested that appraisal is moving from a judgment-based profession to a more scientifically based profession. The authors agree with this observation,

---

1. *The Appraisal of Real Estate*, 12th ed. (Chicago: Appraisal Institute, 2001), 439-441.

although they recommend hanging on to appraisal judgment as a reality test.

The appraisal modeling process, as has been previously discussed, is an attempt to replicate reality, to describe the economic forces that work together to explain the intentions and motivations of human beings in the exchange of real estate. Judgment will always be required in the appraisal process. No matter how much data is available, appraisers will never be able to model everything involved in the real estate market. Some variables will simply not work, no matter how valiant the attempt. A parallel can be seen in the efforts to understand economics in general. Over the course of the last century, economists have attempted to predict and even to influence economic cycles to minimize economic recessions and reduce human suffering. They have been singularly unsuccessful in this regard. The reason, as always, is the uncertainty of human behavior and its serendipitous way of mixing and rationalizing both objective and subjective measures in the decision-making process.

When economists and appraisers fully recognize and understand human nature, we may come to understand how value is set through the interplay of numerous factors of both a qualitative and quantitative nature. In the meantime, we must use judgment to analyze how the complexities of commerce and the result of these elements result in value. Clearly, the melding of appraisal judgment and statistical analysis provides the best of both worlds, leading to a stronger and more supportable valuation.

Statistics can enhance and should never supplant the judgment of observers. Appraisers have always excelled at being keen observers of human behavior. This has been one of the strongest tools of the trade. With the addition of statistical tools to the appraiser's arsenal, the appraisal process can be enhanced and greater accuracy and understanding of valuation patterns can be achieved.

The appraisal profession has been far too limited in its understanding and application of the principles of valuation modeling. The limitations are so significant that we have limited the modeling process to the direct sales comparison approach only and have in many instances refused to acknowledge that this is even an appraisal technique, preferring to name the process *automated valuation modeling* and removing the word *appraisal* from the definition.

The fourth edition of *The Dictionary of Real Estate Appraisal* was one of the first definitive texts to include both *appraisal valuation modeling* and *automated valuation modeling* as suitable definitions for the AVM acronym.

Roads to Competence

There are essentially three avenues that firms or individual appraisers can pursue to gain competence.

1. Learn all about appraisal valuation modeling and develop an in-house AVM system.

2. Learn a great deal about modeling and use someone else's AVM system to augment the valuation process in the firm.

3. Ignore AVM technology and techniques and focus on other areas of the profession.

One of the critical considerations that many firms are currently assessing is how to address the threat and opportunity represented by the increasing acceptance and prevalence of vendor AVMs. Perhaps the best strategy is to explore how employing and integrating statistical techniques and using AVMs appropriately can enhance the competitive position of the firm and the individual appraiser in the marketplace.

If resources are scarce for you or your firm, then the second path, using a vendor's AVM, may be the best choice. There are many AVM products available at low cost on the Internet. Start using these in your appraisal work, to gain experience using the output and learn the strengths and limitations of each product in your market. You will become a better resource for your clients. When the time is right, purchase a statistical software package and start modeling. In the meantime, start saving data in a systematic manner in Excel or some other electronic format so that data can be readily reused and updated.

To further improve your work, expand your knowledge of related fields in your market, including:

* Assessment
* Statistics
* Appraising
* Economics
* Econometrics

The following list could provide a starting point.

1. *Know* how to apply appraisal valuation modeling (AVM) techniques in your everyday work.

2. *Look* at the whole market and learn how to use all available data to value your subject.

3. *Begin* to look at appraisal modeling for what it really is: an enhancement and reorganization of the great skill set that you already have.

4. *Take* a basic statistics course at your local community college or university.

If you take a class in statistics or even enroll in a degree program, you can often purchase software such as Excel, SPSS, or MiniTab at significant savings.

5. *Read* Appraisal Institute publications such as *Valuation Insights & Perspectives* and *The Appraisal Journal* to keep up with the significant changes ahead.

6. *Use* the statistical modeling curriculum already available from the Appraisal Institute and other appraisal organizations.

7. *Apply* these methods *now* in your practice.

8. *Be* confident that you have the knowledge and experience to make this work for you and your clients.

9. *Give* this book to another appraiser or–better yet–make them *buy* it.

CHAPTER 12

Resource Guide

"*The most valuable commodity I know of is information. I don't throw darts at a board. I bet on sure things.*"

–Michael Douglas, *Wall Street* (1987)

"*Roads? Where we're going we don't need roads.*"

–Christopher Lloyd, *Back to the Future* (1985)

This handbook is not meant to replace a standard statistics textbook, which should be a fundamental reference. Nor will it replace an understanding of basic appraisal principles and practices. Rather, it should be seen as a supplement to such knowledge and a guide through specific issues and problems.

Your first step towards competence is complete with the reading of this book. The next step involves integrating this knowledge into your workflow and toolbox. The following resources should assist you greatly in this exciting (and scary) new appraisal world we face. All have been used by one or more of the authors and all are recommended.

Books on Statistics

Appraisers need to consider both classes and texts to augment their knowledge. While there are numerous books on statistics that a student may consult, it is critical that the text be accessible and appropriate for the career professional. Each of the following texts is useful and appropriate for those who wish to examine statistical techniques on their own. The authors have carefully considered the manner in which the narrative material is presented and selected the following texts from more than 40 books.

In this book, we have identified some basics of statistical analysis. The purpose of statistical analysis is to identify, calculate, and interpret phenomena. To be studied, these transactions (and the variables involved) must be clearly defined and understood. The importance of appraisal knowledge and experience to the proper incorporation of statistical analysis in the appraisal process is clear. Appraisal theory, not statistical theory, always drives the process.

A Guide to Appraisal Valuation Modeling

By Mark R. Linné, MAI, CRE, CAE, M. Steven Kane, and George Dell, MAI, SRA

Chicago: Appraisal Institute, 2000

This introductory guide, written by two of the authors of this text along with George Dell, MAI, SRA, provides an overview of the entire appraisal valuation modeling process. It focuses on introducing readers to the mathematical modeling of market behavior. The handbook provides historical perspectives, statistical fundamentals, support for assertions of causality in appraisal reports, and the basics of regression analysis and model construction. Throughout the text, the authors highlight the interplay of evolving statistical theory, traditional appraisal standards and practices, and simple common sense. This text is presently used in numerous academic venues, including the Appraisal Institute's AVM seminar, and in valuation and statistics courses at the college level, including Texas A&M University.

The Cartoon Guide to Statistics

By Larry Golnick and Woolcott Smith

New York: Harper Perennial, 1993

This book is perhaps the most reader-friendly text available on the subject of statistics. The book is engaging and provides excellent insight and background for the reader, covering all of the central ideas of modern statistics, including the summary and display of data, probability in gambling and medicine, random variables, Bernoulli trials, the central limit theorem, hypothesis testing, confidence interval estimation, and much more. The text is easy to read and the illustrations provide humor and aid understanding.

Statistics for the Utterly Confused

By Lloyd R. Jaisingh, PhD

New York: McGraw-Hill, 2000

Like *The Cartoon Guide to Statistics*, this book provides a reader-friendly introduction to statistics. It is especially written for students in introductory, non-calculus-based courses and is targeted towards professionals who use statistics in the workplace. The author is a teacher, and the text is written to enhance understanding. The multiple-choice questions at the end of each chapter help readers gauge how well they have grasped the essentials of the statistical material.

Introduction to Statistics
By Susan F. Wagner, PhD
New York: HarperCollins Publishers, Inc., 1992

This text is touted as a college outline text, and while it is not as engaging as the texts previously described, it is nonetheless a fairly easy read. It provides a comprehensive outline of statistics in a narrative format and can be used to supplement other texts. The book is very well indexed and includes practice problems and solutions.

Statistics Made Simple
By H.T. Hayslett, Jr., M.S.
New York: Broadway Books, 2001

This guide provides a concise and straightforward introduction to statistics and a platform for understanding essential principles with only a basic algebra background. The text has exercises in each chapter that help the reader review the concepts presented. In addition, the text contains step-by-step directions for applying statistical techniques.

The Complete Idiot's Guide to Business Statistics
By Sunny Baker, PhD
Indianapolis: Pearson Education Company, 2002

Similar to the last two texts described, this text uses both cartoon graphics and easily understood statistical presentations to present the major topics in statistics painlessly. This book is focused more towards business statistics than the other texts, and this provides a real-world framework that is helpful to appraisers.

Statistics: Crash Course
By Murray R. Spiegel and David P. Lindstrom
New York: McGraw-Hill, 2000

This text is part of Schaum's Outline Series, and it provides a condensed and abridged version of a larger text, *Outline of Theory and Problems of Statistics.* The book is designed for quick, effective study, and, though abridged, it covers all of the statistics necessary to the real estate appraiser.

Conquering Statistics: Numbers Without the Crunch
By Jefferson Hane Weaver
Cambridge, Mass.: Perseus Publishing, 2000

This book is an excellent introduction to statistics. Unlike the other books in this survey, it relies primarily on narrative, with no equations and virtually no mathematical formulae. The text tells the story behind the statistics and provides a fascinating historical backdrop and understanding of why these numerical tools are important. The book is written for the statistically scared, and uses simple mathematical principles to break down the often confusing concepts behind probabilities, means, and samples.

Multiple Regression: A Primer
By Paul D. Allison
Thousand Oaks, Calif.: Pine Forge Press, 1999

This text introduces readers to situations in which multiple regression can provide insights. The book is constructed in a question-and-answer format and uses modules to provide instruction on specific areas of statistics. Though the book focuses on methods for the social sciences, the presentation is appropriate for a broad-based introduction to basic statistical methods.

A Mathematician Reads the Newspaper
By John Allen Paulos
New York: Anchor Press, 1995

Less a book on statistics than an analysis of how numbers can be misunderstood, this text is an interesting examination of how a lack of statistical knowledge can hinder a reader's understanding of even the simplest statistics encountered every day.

Statistics Without Tears: A Primer for Non-Mathematicians
By Derek Rowntree
New York: Charles Scribner's & Sons, 1981

This book is a fine mix to help readers understand statistics and the role statistics plays in our everyday lives. The text operates on the principle that statistics can be learned without having to perform calculations. The book introduces the basic concepts and terminology of statistics, explaining the theory of statistics before getting involved in the associated calculations.

Reading Between the Numbers: Statistical Thinking in Everyday Life
By Joseph Tal, PhD
New York: McGraw Hill, 2001

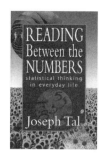

The goal of this text is to bring statistics down to earth for the average reader. The book focuses on the story and psychology behind the numbers we see in our everyday lives. The book also provides an understanding of the manner in which statistics are used in our decision making.

Statistics for Real Estate Professionals
By Rebecca F. Guy and Louis G. Pol
New York: Quorum Books, 1989

This excellent text is the only book in our survey that specifically examines statistics as it relates to real estate and valuation. The text focuses on the role that statistics plays in measuring neighborhood change, economic value, market effects, and fluctuations and variances in the value of real estate. It provides a strong introduction to statistics and then covers descriptive statistics, index construction, probability, the normal distribution, sampling, and inferential statistics. This is a superb book and should be one of the first read by those who want to integrate statistics and real estate. It should be noted that this book is out of print and may be difficult to obtain.

Reasoning with Statistics: How to Read Quantitative Research
By Frederick Williams
New York: Holt, Rinehart, and Winston, Inc., 1991

This text is intended for students interested in understanding quantitative methods with a focus on the social sciences. Given this focus, the book provides a good explanation of statistics without resorting to complex formulae.

Statistics: Addison Wesley Review Series
By Julie Sawyer
Boston: Addison Wesley, 2002

This book is a review of basic statistics and provides a good outline with questions at the end of each chapter. It should be used in tandem with one of the other texts noted above to gain a full understanding of statistical methods.

Statistics the Easy Way
By Douglas Downing, PhD, and Jeffrey Clark, PhD
Hauppauge, N.Y.: Barron's Educational Series, Inc., 1997

> This text provides the fundamentals of statistical theory and applications. The book is especially relevant for those who have limited knowledge of mathematics and is structured with exercises and questions with answers at the end of each chapter. This is a good book that covers all of the elements that are needed to understand and apply statistical techniques.

Against the Gods: The Remarkable Story of Risk
By Peter L. Bernstein
New York: John Wiley & Sons, Inc., 1996

> This remarkable book provides an overview of the origins of statistics and strong biographical information about those who pioneered the development of the statistical techniques that we use today. The book is an interesting treatment of the subject that underscores the human element in the statistical process.

Forgotten Statistics
By Douglas Downing, PhD, and Jeffrey Clark, PhD
Hauppauge, N.Y.: Barron's Educational Series, Inc., 1996

> This text is intended to help readers who have taken a course in statistics to "rediscover" the subject. It is also useful for those who need a concise introduction to statistics.

Structured Statistical Training

The texts described in the previous section offer excellent introductions to statistics for a broad range of students. Books also have the virtue of accommodating a self-paced introduction to subject matter. For many students, however, independent study is not conducive to an understanding of statistical methodology. Additionally, the inability to ask questions can lead to anxiety that precludes true understanding.

A solution for many is the structured training environment of the classroom. For the appraiser seeking statistical and modeling training, there are ample courses available from professional organizations, statistical software vendors, and educational institutions.

Educational Institutions

Local community colleges are often overlooked, but they offer excellent training in statistical methodology. A random search through a representative sampling of community college curricula shows that

introductory statistics courses are offered at most
local educational institutions. These institutions are
numerous in most mid-sized and smaller communities, and they have the virtues of low cost, easy acces-
sibility, and limited complexity.

A four-year institution might also offer appropriate course work. Though generally more costly than
a community college, these institutions have structured statistical training that is geared for beginning,
intermediate, and advanced students.

Finally, there are many excellent post-graduate
courses offered by universities throughout the country. Of note is a statistics class taught at the University
of St. Thomas in Minneapolis, Minnesota. This one-
week course is part of the master's degree program in
real estate appraisal. It covers basic principles in statistical analysis, with a hands-on approach using
Minitab. The course is taught every other summer at
the business school in downtown Minneapolis.

Software Vendor Training

There are numerous vendors of statistical software
that also offer training at surprisingly reasonable
cost. While the training is usually specific to the software of the vendor, these courses offer statistical
training coupled with the hands-on use of analytical
techniques within the specific software that simpli-
fies the statistical process.

Statistical Package for the Social Sciences (SPSS)

SPSS is the nation's leading statistical software and is
the software most often used by the assessment community in performing computer-assisted mass
appraisal. In addition to the software, SPSS offers a
comprehensive training program that encompasses
basic statistics.

SPSS for Windows: Basic

Course description: This course allows the student to get up to speed in SPSS quickly and easily
in a two-day course. Students learn the basics of
data definition, data analysis, and presentation of
results. They learn how to get data into SPSS so
that they can focus on analyzing the information.
In addition to the fundamentals, shortcuts are
demonstrated that will help save time. This course
is designed with the SPSS beginner in mind.

Who should attend: Anyone who will be using
SPSS for Windows for data analysis. Especially
useful for those new to using a statistical package
for data analysis or to the Windows environment.

Also recommended for those considering purchasing SPSS for Windows.

Prerequisites: Familiarity with Windows environment. Experience with other Windows programs helpful. Experience with SPSS not necessary, although a basic understanding of the purpose and functions of the software is helpful.

Course content:
- Crosstabulation tables
- Multiple response variables
- Helpful features: syntax, data templates, data dictionary
- Introduction to SPSS for Windows
- Recoding and computing new variables
- Printing and saving output
- Entering data directly into SPSS data editor
- Assigning missing value codes
- Getting started in SPSS for Windows
- Adding variable and value labels
- Opening Excel, Dbase, and fixed-format ASCII files
- Choosing appropriate statistics
- Graphs: pies, bars, and scatter plots

Statistical Analysis Using SPSS

Course description: In this three-day course students have a chance to focus on the statistical component of SPSS. This is an application-oriented course and the approach is practical. Students have a chance to examine several statistical techniques and discuss situations in which each technique is appropriate, the assumptions made in each method, how to set up the analysis using SPSS, and how to interpret the results.

Who should attend: Anyone who has worked with SPSS for Windows and wants to become better versed in its statistical capabilities. Anyone who wants to expand their knowledge of appropriate statistical procedures.

Prerequisites: On-the-job experience with SPSS for Windows or completion of the Windows basic and/or intermediate courses. Basic statistical knowledge or at least one college-level course in statistics. For users of SPSS for Windows Base System.

Course content:
- Influence of sample size

- Data checking
- Describing categorical data
- Comparing groups: categorical data
- Exploratory data analysis: interval scale data
- Mean differences between groups I: simple case
- Mean differences between groups II: one-factor ANOVA
- Mean differences between groups III: two-factor ANOVA
- Bivariate plots and statistics
- Introduction to regression

Advanced Statistical Analysis Using SPSS

Course description: In this three-day seminar students consider in depth some of the more advanced statistical procedures available in SPSS. They examine several advanced statistical techniques and discuss situations when each may be used, the assumptions made by each method, how to set up the analysis using SPSS, and how to interpret the results.

Who should attend: Anyone who has worked with SPSS for Windows and wants to become better versed in the more advanced statistical capabilities of SPSS for Windows. Anyone who has a solid understanding of statistics and wants to expand their knowledge of appropriate statistical procedures and how to set them up using SPSS.

Prerequisites: On-the-job statistical experience or completion of the Statistical Analysis Using SPSS and/or intermediate SPSS for Windows courses. Advanced statistical knowledge or at least two college-level courses in statistics. SPSS for Windows Base System, SPSS Advanced Statistics, SPSS Professional Statistics.

Course content:
- Overview
- Discriminant analysis
- Binary logistic regression
- Multinomial logistic regression
- Survival analysis (Kaplan-Meier)
- MANOVA: multivariate analysis of variance
- Loglinear analysis
- Cluster analysis
- Factor analysis
- Repeated measures ANOVA

MINITAB

Offering an alternative to SPSS, MINITAB can also be a statistical software resource. One-day training sessions are offered on the mechanics of the software and on the use of a variety of statistical problem-solving techniques. All courses are offered both on-site and publicly. MINITAB is a Windows application, and a good working knowledge of Windows is required for all courses. The following list of available courses is recommended for individuals and companies.

Introduction to MINITAB

Course description: This course allows users to begin to navigate quickly through the software and properly structure data. It also provides an overview of the use and manipulation of graphics, basic statistical assessment, and sample size determinations.

Prerequisite: Experience with MINITAB is not necessary for this course.

Basic Statistics

Course description: The emphasis of this course is good business decision making based on the application of statistics. This course further explores the software in order to make users

1. More efficient with MINITAB's powerful tactical tools
2. Better able to determine appropriate sample sizes
3. Able to test the relationships between variables using correlation, regression, and matrix plots

Prerequisite: Introduction to MINITAB.

Statistical Quality Analysis

Course description: The main objectives of this course include measurement system evaluation, process capability, and process stability. Estimates of variation are presented in the form of hands-on examples of various statistical frameworks:

- Process variation versus tolerance
- Range method versus standard deviation
- Within-subgroup, between-subgroup, and overall

Prerequisite: Introduction to MINITAB, Basic Statistics.

Factorial DOE

Course description: The scope of this course is centered on MINITAB's DOE interface, which can create full and fractional factorial designs. Pareto charts are interpreted along with normal plots of effects, including the interaction of plots in combination with tabulated statistical output. Settings are chosen to optimize responses or determine a direction for additional experimentation.

Prerequisite: Introduction to MINITAB, Basic Statistics.

DOE in Practice

Course description: As an extension of the Factorial DOE course, this course deals with situations where classic factorial or response surface design and analysis are not possible. It analyzes experiments with missing data, factors that are hard to change, and variables that may affect the response but cannot be controlled. Taguchi's approaches to robust design and Plackett-Burman experiments are also incorporated into this course. With a customizable course content, the length can be one or two days.

Prerequisite: Introduction to MINITAB, Basic Statistics, Factorial DOE.

Response Surface Experiments

Course description: Including central composite and Box-Behnken designs, this course goes beyond the basic 2k factorial designs. The impact of curvature, center points, and quadratic effects are evaluated along with sequential experimentation.

Prerequisite: Introduction to MINITAB, Basic Statistics, Factorial DOE.

Reliability Analysis–Introduction

Course description: Introductory reliability analysis techniques are used in this course to determine the lifetime of a product. Strong emphasis is placed upon choosing distributions. Common distributions are explored to model failure rates. This course adds to the user's tool set by presenting nonparametric techniques.

Prerequisite: Introduction to MINITAB, Basic Statistics.

Reliability Analysis–Advanced Topics

Course description: As it expands upon the introductory course on reliability, this course examines censored and uncensored data, explanatory variables on product lifetime, failure estimates on product fleets, and regression with life data, risk analysis, and accelerated life testing.

Prerequisite: Introduction to MINITAB, Basic Statistics, Reliability Analysis–Introduction.

Mixture Experiments

Course description: This course introduces the student to mixture experiments and blending properties using trace, contour, and surface plots. The formulation that optimizes one or more responses is identified.

Prerequisite: Introduction to MINITAB, Basic Statistics, Factorial DOE.

The following courses are recommended for individuals and companies in financial services, human resources departments, and other areas that use metrics such as time, defect rates, and revenue data.

Service Quality–Introduction to MINITAB

Course description: This course introduces the student to importing projects and worksheets and structuring data for manipulation. Similar to the other (i.e., not service quality) introductory course, basic graphs and charts are created, and macros are used to automate data analysis.

Prerequisite: Experience with MINITAB is not necessary for this course.

Service Quality–Basic Statistical Tools

Course description: This course builds on the introductory course by adding key statistical concepts, sample size requirements, multiple comparisons, and variable relationships. Simple and multiple linear regressions are explored.

Prerequisite: Service Quality–Introduction to MINITAB.

Service Quality–Statistical Quality Analysis

Course description: Additional software features are examined to teach students to evaluate measurement systems, investigate process capability, and implement continuous data techniques including

- Gage R&R; X, -S, and I-MR charts
- Normal capability analysis
- Normal capability analysis with Box-Cox transformation
- Weibull capability analysis

Prerequisite: Service Quality–Introduction to MINITAB, Basic Statistical Tools.

Service Quality–MINITAB Advanced Topics

Course description: Risk is evaluated using odds ratios, and the differences in factor levels are identified using multiple comparison tests and graphical procedures. Model violations are assessed for key assumptions that affect model reliability. Part of this course incorporates StatGuide LIVE, which involves student contributions in the form of data to apply with the techniques learned and to evaluate the analysis through the produced responses.

Prerequisite: Service Quality–Introduction to MINITAB, Basic Statistical Tools.

Private Mass Appraisal/Modeling Instruction

In addition to vendors, other training is available from private companies specializing in training on statistical techniques and modeling methodologies. One of the best in this limited field is Thimgan and Associates.

The Center for Valuation Economics

Conceived as an umbrella educational provider offering specialized and focused educational training, The Center for Valuation Economics (CVE) has developed curricula that support both residential and commercial valuation. CVE is developing a certification program in both residential and commercial modeling that will permit students to attain and demonstrate proficiency through a combination of course work, hands-on computer training with SPSS, and case studies that incorporate actual real estate data, permitting students to solve real-world appraisal problems. The analysis focuses on modeling applications for real estate data. These are the only curricula available that provide training in both residential and commercial applications for both private-sector and assessment practitioners.

Thimgan and Associates

Thimgan and Associates provides a number of courses directed specifically towards an understanding of mass appraisal and appraisal valuation modeling. The courses are taught by Garth Thimgan, Robert Gloudemans, and James Thimgan, three of the nation's leading experts in this field. The company offers three distinct courses, each focusing on introductory, intermediate, and advanced modeling applications.

Introduction to SPSS for Appraisers

This one-day session is essential for anyone wanting basic training with SPSS's Version 11 software. It is designed for the complete novice and is recommended for students with limited or no exposure to SPSS. The workshop is tailored toward mass appraisal and assessment. It begins by exploring SPSS, which includes an introduction to the main windows that are used during an SPSS session. Each window is defined and the appropriate applications are explained and demonstrated. Once the students have completely explored the various windows, they are introduced to data analysis. Here the student is taught to compute, recode, and transform variables. In addition, students learn to develop frequency tables, descriptives, and crosstabs and to compare means. Also, students learn to select specified cases from the data file, summarize information, and develop reports. Graphs and charts are a major component of SPSS, and the students are shown how to use the various charts and graphs available in SPSS. The latter part of the day provides the students with lab exercises, which allow them to apply the various applications demonstrated in the earlier sessions. All applications use actual property databases, providing the students with demonstrations and hands-on lab exercises.

Fundamentals of Modeling with SPSS

This is an intensive four-day workshop on mass appraisal model building using SPSS for Windows. Topics include

- Generating statistics
- Analyzing, graphing, and stratifying market data
- Developing and refining MRA models for residential properties

All applications use actual property databases, providing the students with demonstrations and hands-on lab exercises.

Intermediate Residential Modeling with SPSS

This intensive four-day workshop takes participants through advanced residential model development using SPSS for Windows. Additional topics include

- Sales ratio testing using the new SPSS Version 11 ratio options
- Application of models to the universe of properties
- Interface with GIS

All applications use actual property databases, providing the students with demonstrations and hands-on lab exercises.

Modeling Vacant Land and Commercial Properties

This four-day workshop focuses on modeling vacant land and multifamily and commercial properties. Topics include

- Sales screening and analysis
- Stratification and identification of market and submarket areas
- Determining model structures
- Variable transformations
- Nonlinear models
- Modeling various property types

The workshop uses SPSS for Windows Version 11.

Appraisal Institute

As the leading professional association of real estate appraisers, the Appraisal Institute has always been at the forefront of appraisal education, providing its members and professionals in related disciplines with educational programs and publications that serve as the industry standard. Historically, the organization has viewed the emergence of AVMs with skepticism and caution, but in recent years it has begun to offer its members training to update their skills and adapt to the changing workplace. In addition to its introductory AVM seminar, the Appraisal Institute debuts a two-day course on statistics, real estate finance, and valuation modeling in 2004.

Appraisal Valuation Modeling

This seminar is based on the Appraisal Institute's publication *A Guide to Appraisal Valuation Modeling* and was developed by M. Steven Kane. It covers a variety of introductory statistics and includes the following topics:

- Computer-assisted mass appraisal
- Automated valuation modeling
- Appraisal valuation modeling
- Regression modeling

On completion of this seminar, the student should be able to

1. Use a line chart (polygon) to show several variables simultaneously
2. Use a polygon to show the same variable for different strata

3. Understand the basic mechanics of regression analysis

4. Understand and interpret outcome statistics from valuation models

5. Present results in a comprehensive and understandable format for use in appraisal reports

6. Apply regression analysis in cost, sales comparison, and income capitalization models

7. Distinguish between model specification and calibration

Statistics, Real Estate Finance, and Valuation Modeling

This two-day course provides an introduction to statistics, real estate finance, and modeling with applications to residential and commercial real estate appraisal. The first day concentrates on statistical analysis and modeling while the second covers real estate finance.

On completion of the course, the student should be able to

- Calculate means, medians, and modes and explain their relative strengths and weaknesses as measures of central tendency

- Explain what regression analysis can and cannot do, how a regression model works and how regression relates to traditional sales comparison

- Calculate regression statistics and interpret the results of regression estimates

- Explain and apply index models

- Understand the competency for statistical analysis required under USPAP

International Association of Assessing Officers

As the professional association for assessment officials, IAAO offers both real estate fundamentals and courses specific to computer-assisted mass appraisal (CAMA) and appraisal valuation modeling (AVM). These courses, while focused on assessment procedures, offer much for fee appraisers as well. While offering the same single-property appraisal curriculum for its members as the Appraisal Institute, IAAO has also created a comprehensive educational program that focuses on the modeling process. Mass appraisal courses are usually offered across the country and throughout the year. These courses focus on assessment methodology, but also provide an excellent introduction to statistical techniques. IAAO offers advanced courses in both residential and commercial modeling techniques. Often overlooked, these courses provide an excellent opportunity to obtain competency in modeling in an appraisal environment.

Course 300: Fundamentals of Mass Appraisal

This course provides an introduction to mass appraisal and is a prerequisite for the 300 series of courses offered by IAAO. Topics covered include

- Single-property appraisal versus mass appraisal
- Components of a mass appraisal system
- Data requirements and analysis
- Introduction to statistics
- Use of assessment ratio studies in mass appraisal
- Modeling of the three approaches to value
- Selection of a mass appraisal system

Course 310: Applications of Mass Appraisal Fundamentals

This residential and commercial application course builds on the theories and concepts taught in Course 300. It uses case studies to demonstrate key concepts in a real-world setting. The course provides students with practical applications of the tools and techniques presented in Course 300.

Course 311: Residential Modeling Concepts

Course 311 presents a detailed study of the mass appraisal process as applied to residential property. Topics covered include

- A comparison of single-property appraisal and mass appraisal
- The major steps in the mass appraisal process
- Data requirements
- Market analysis
- Application of the approaches to value
- Use of sales ratio studies
- Valuation review techniques

Course 312: Commercial/Industrial Modeling Concepts

Course 312 presents a detailed study of the mass appraisal process as applied to income-producing property. Topics include

- Income property data
- Market analysis

- Sales comparison approach
- Income capitalization approach
- Cost approach
- Gross and net income analysis
- Capitalization rate development
- Model specification and calibration
- Value review and maintenance

Course 320: Multiple Regression Analysis

Course 320 is an introductory offering designed to provide intensive training in the application of multiple regression analysis. The course is built in a Windows environment and uses SPSS for demonstrations. Course 320 introduces the basic functions necessary to analyze a database. Students learn how to develop frequency distributions, crosstabulations, and averages and how to use various graphs to display the results of the analysis. They also learn how to develop an additive multiple regression model using stepwise regression, what regression statistics mean, and how to interpret them. Finally, students test the results of the model once it has been developed and learn how to use the multiple regression analysis to calibrate a cost model market.

Course 322: Application of Residential Modeling Concepts

Course 322 provides students with a hands-on computerized learning environment for developing and applying automated valuation models. Using a Windows-based statistical software package, students work in computer labs each day, developing and exploring computer applications for the cost and sales comparison approaches to value. Analysis includes the use of summary statistics, crosstabulation reports, scatter plots, box plots, and curve-fitting functions. Students learn how to develop appropriate adjustments for location, size of structure, quality grade, and depreciation. The three basic model structures (additive, log-linear, and hybrid) are developed and calibrated with techniques like multiple regression analysis, non-linear multiple regression analysis, and feedback. All valuation models are measured against the performance standards in the IAAO Standard on Ratio Studies. Spatial analysis and response surface location adjustments are introduced in this course. Those attending will learn better ways to explain and defend the mass appraisal models.

The Internet provides a significant number of on-line courses of varying quality and ease of use.

Appendix

All appraisers, especially those who wish to have an understanding of the various aspects of AVM development, processing, and application, should read and understand three documents:

- *Uniform Standards of Professional Appraisal Practice*, Advisory Opinion 18: Use of an Automated Valuation Model
- International Association of Assessing Officers *Standard on Ratio Studies*
- *International Valuation Standards*, Exposure Draft of the Proposed International Valuation Application: Mass Appraisal of Real Property

The first document specifically addresses AVMs, while the other two relate to the establishment of guidelines to promulgate standards for the valuation of real property within the framework of mass appraisal.

Advisory Opinion 18: Use of an Automated Valuation Model

The document that may already be familiar to appraisers is USPAP Advisory Opinion 18: Use of an Automated Valuation Model. This document provides appropriate guidelines and is an important first step provided by The Appraisal Foundation to lay the groundwork for the manner in which the profession positions itself with respect to AVMs.

References

- *Uniform Standards of Professional Appraisal Practice*, Advisory Opinion 18: Use of an Automated Valuation Model (AVM). Washington, D.C.: The Appraisal Foundation (www.appraisalfoundation.org), approved 1997.
- *Standard on Ratio Studies*. Chicago: International Association of Assessing Officers (www.iaao.org), approved July 1999.
- *International Valuation Standards*. Exposure Draft of Proposed International Valuation Application: Mass Appraisal of Real Property. London: International Valuation Standards Committee (www.ivsc.org), December 2002.

IAAO Standard on Ratio Standards

The *Standard for Ratio Studies* published by the International Association of Assessing Officers provides the guidelines that govern assessment practice throughout the world. It is an essential reference for those who are involved in the valuation of real property using computer-assisted mass appraisal (CAMA).

IVSC Mass Appraisal of Real Property

The third set of guidelines are those within the Exposure Draft of the International Valuation Application on the Mass Appraisal of Real Property, promulgated by the International Valuation Standards Committee. The International Valuation Standards Committee is a non-governmental organization (NGO) member of the United Nations. It works cooperatively with member states, organizations such as the World Bank, OECD, International Federation of Accountants, International Accounting Standards Board, and others including valuation societies throughout the world to harmonize and promote agreement and understanding of valuation standards.

According to the IVSC, its principal objective is to formulate and publish, in the public interest, valuation standards and procedural guidance for the valuation of assets for use in financial statements and to promote their worldwide acceptance and observance. The second objective is to harmonize standards among the world's states and to disclose differences in standards statements and applications of standards as they occur.

The IVSC notes that international standards are critical to the stability of worldwide financial transactions. International appraisal methodologies and standards will filter down to national and local appraisal standards. National standards-setting bodies seek to influence what is occurring internationally and provide guidelines that are consistent throughout the world.

The second quarter IVSC 2000 report notes that standards are now being further extended and developed to form a single benchmark that meets the needs of users, capital markets, regulators, national valuation and appraisal institutes, and individual members throughout the world. The report goes on to note that investors, regulators, and users of valuation require consistency, clarity, reliability, and transparency in valuation reporting worldwide.

In August 2002, and again in December 2002, the IVSC Standards Board released an exposure draft of a proposed International Valuation Application on mass appraisal of real property. While this initial document currently covers mass appraisal for property taxation, the board will consider whether the coverage should be expanded and the most appropriate way to do this.

Relevance

While both the IAAO and IVSC documents pertain to the assessment of real property for taxation purposes, the guidelines and relevant empirical measures of accuracy are important foundational guidelines that all AVM and CAMA practitioners should be aware of and use in the valuation process. Ultimately, the valuation of real property using these techniques must be uniformly applied, considered, and measured if uniformity and equity are to be maintained.

One additional factor to consider is the clear evidence that organizations that begin to define CAMA standards for property tax purposes eventually extend their purview to the development of standards for the private sector. This is evident most notably with the IVSC, which will determine in the near future if real property appraisal standards should be extended from their current property tax focus to private uses in lending and asset valuation.

In a similar vein, IAAO has established an AVM Standard Ad Hoc Committee (similar to its Ad Hoc Committee on Computer-Assisted Mass Appraisal in 1991) that will seek to establish standards for the private sector. While this activity is somewhat unusual for IAAO, it demonstrates that some appraisal organizations see a clear need for the establishment of standards for AVM use and development. In the absence of any private sector standards outside of The Appraisal Foundation's Advisory Opinion 18, IAAO and other organizations will take advantage of the vacuum and seek to establish standards that can be used to guide those who develop, evaluate, and use AVMs in the private sector.

It is critical that institutions such as the Appraisal Institute work with AVM users, developers, and other parties to promulgate standards sufficient to guide its membership and other appraisal professionals. Appraisers must take the initiative to be at the forefront of this development and not abrogate their responsibility at this opportune time, ensuring that appraisers can take full advantage of AVM technologies and techniques in the future. Appraisers must consider the lessons of the past and be the driving force in the future development of AVM applications. The profession must not be content to let others develop these guidelines and standards. Rather, it must ensure that the acronym AVM is universally recognized as *appraisal valuation modeling*, underscoring the fact that it is the expertise of the appraisal community that provides AVM users with the valuation accuracy and validation that permits the advancement of the profession.

To do any less, is to abandon our role in guiding the profession to its next logical step, which is the control of the process and procedures used to determine valuation on a worldwide basis. Appraisers have a window of opportunity. They must seize the initiative before that window closes.

"It is easy to lie with statistics, but it's a whole lot easier to lie without them."

–attributed to Richard J. Hernstein
by his colleague Charles Murray